THE SNOW QUEEN

THE SNOW QUEEN

by

SURIA MAGITO and RUDOLF WEIL

Based on the story by Hans Andersen

With an Introduction by
MICHEL SAINT-DENIS

HEINEMANN EDUCATIONAL
BOOKS LTD · LONDON

Heinemann Educational Books Ltd

LONDON MELBOURNE TORONTO
SINGAPORE JOHANNESBURG
EDINBURGH NEW DELHI
HONG KONG NAIROBI
AUCKLAND IBADAN

THE AUTHORS OF THE ENGLISH VERSION WOULD LIKE
TO ACKNOWLEDGE THEIR INDEBTEDNESS TO MR. EUGENE
SCHWARTZ AND TO HIS DRAMATISATION IN RUSSIAN OF
"THE SNOW QUEEN"

ISBN 0 435 23570 2

FIRST PUBLISHED 1951
REPRINTED 1955, 1957, 1959, 1961, 1965
NEW EDITION 1967
REPRINTED 1970

PUBLISHED BY
HEINEMANN EDUCATIONAL BOOKS LTD
48 CHARLES STREET, LONDON WIX 8AH
PRINTED OFFSET LITHO AND BOUND IN GREAT BRITAIN
BY COX & WYMAN LTD, LONDON,
FAKENHAM AND READING

CONTENTS

CHARACTERS

THE STORYTELLER
GERDA, a girl
KAY, a boy, her friend
THE CHANCELLOR
GERDA'S GRANDMOTHER
THE SNOW QUEEN
KARL, a Raven
KLARA, another Raven
PRINCESS CHRISTINA
PRINCE KLAUS
THE KING
THE ROBBER WOMAN
WENKI, her daughter
BARBRO, a Robber
OLOF, another Robber
THE REINDEER

Robbers, Guards, Lackeys, Polar Bears

First performed by The Young Vic company of The Old Vic Theatre, and produced in that theatre in 1948, with the following cast:

THE STORYTELLER	Pierre Lefevre
GERDA, a girl	Christine Hearne
KAY, a boy, her friend	James Wellman
THE CHANCELLOR	Duncan Ross
GERDA'S GRANDMOTHER	Sheila Ballantine
THE SNOW QUEEN	Jean Wilson
KARL, a Raven	Powys Thomas
KLARA, another Raven	Ann Morrish
PRINCESS CHRISTINA	Tarn Bassett
PRINCE KLAUS	Edgar Wreford
THE KING	Anthony Van Bridge
THE ROBBER WOMAN	Mervyn Blake
WENKI, her daughter	June Vincent
BARBRO, a Robber	Peter Duguid
OLOF, another Robber	Edgar Wreford
THE REINDEER	Veronica Wells

Robbers, Guards, Lackeys, Polar Bears played by: Shaun O'Riordan, Peter Retey, Peter Duguid, Jack Ralphs, David Woodman and Edgar Wreford.

The Music specially composed by Henry Boys

Decor by Motley

Produced by Michel Saint-Denis and Suria Magito

INTRODUCTION

By Michel Saint-Denis

ACTING for children, if it is undertaken in the wrong spirit, easily becomes a mockery. An audience of children is the most free, and, in many ways, the easiest in the world to please: a child is ready to accept everything; hence it is easy to take advantage of his credulity, to impose on him and to dazzle him. On the other hand, it is far from easy to win his confidence and to hold his attention on the action which takes place before him. A child is demanding: to keep him interested, that is to say attentive, he must believe in the story he is being told and must believe in it all the time. The field of his confidence knows no bounds, because he lives in a world of imagination. In his own games, he turns everything and everybody, beginning with himself, into instruments to give reality to his invention: thus a stool becomes a tree, a piece of rag is a sail, and he himself is the monkey or the explorer climbing the tree, the wind filling the sails or the sailor at the helm. Once the game has begun, the child plays *seriously*: his body, his voice are literally moulded by his imagination; he is very often terrified by his own inventions, and runs to his mother for protection from the lion of his own creation which is now chasing him—though at the same time he loves the danger of it.

To make children act among themselves, and to act for them, are obviously very different tasks. In my opinion, it is not possible *for children to act* before an audience, however small, without its destroying an essential part of their performance. Success in *acting for children* lies in creating on the stage this faith in the reality of fiction which every child has experienced in himself and the joy and thrill of which he hopes to find again in the theatre.

To achieve this, one must first, like the child himself, play *seriously*. By means of ingenuity and technical ability, of naivety and skill, the actors have to re-discover that spontaneity which often makes a child a superb *born* actor. The production of a play like THE SNOW QUEEN depends primarily on the ability of the producer to kindle in himself and in his actors a childlike outlook, for if either he or the actors feel any embarrassment, the play runs the risk of appearing *childish* or of becoming over-burdened with complicated effects.

This play is a fairy tale. In it we find human beings whom we can recognise, and for whom, from the rise of the curtain, we feel sympathy. These are Gerda, Kay and the old Granny. With them, we are going to venture into an unfamiliar world, which will be disturbing and even rather frightening, because it is magic: the world of the Snow Queen, the Chancellor, the King, the Prince and Princess. With Gerda, we shall visit the lair of savage robbers who plunder and kill, and at each stage of her journey she will be helped on her way by animals far more sensitive to the trials and tribulations of humans than one might expect, for these animals, like the reindeer and the two ravens, are able to talk, and, although it is too cold for them to do anything but growl and croak, even the polar bears and birds can make us understand what their feelings are.

This is all very well, you will say, but we are in a theatre. All these creatures and characters will want costumes; the action of the play goes from a garret to a king's palace, to a

robbers' cave and so to the climax in the Ice Palace of the
Snow Queen, before returning in the end to the garret—
without counting the many scenes in the open air. The play
calls for extremely mobile scenery.

I admit the difficulties are great. At first, it seems impossible to stage the play without using some machinery for
changing the scenery in view of the audience, or at least for
making very rapid changes. It seems so important also to
give an impression of the different roads, cross-roads and
snow fields where Gerda gets lost on her journey. Then the
seasons themselves change; Gerda travels from the relatively
warm south to the frozen north, and, what is more, the play
starts in the heart of winter, and ends with the coming of
spring. We cannot help seeing the King's Palace as a grand,
sinister place: this set should be high, so that the small Gerda
is lost in its cold vastness. And what of the Palace of the
Snow Queen, with its glittering stalactites, through which
Gerda must pass, before she catches a glimpse of her friend
Kay perched high on a throne of ice? She manages to melt
his heart, to lead him away from the palace, and in an instant
the palace disappears, to give place to the exit closely guarded
by fierce animals. The change from one scene to the other,
from the inside to the outside of the palace, calls for nothing
short of a miracle. It seems that only the cinema could suc-
ceed here, unless one had a revolving stage—with music,
lighting effects, wind and snow to accompany the change.
Thus the difficulties lead us to dream of using means which
we do not possess—means which are in fact those of the
pantomime whose magnificent transformation scenes en-
chant us every Christmas.

Such technical wonders often have children paralysed in
their seats—I have seen them gaping, eyes popping out of

their heads, and stupefied. But however much a show of this size dominates children, it does not *touch* them. It is as if they were faced with toys too complicated, too perfect, to be played with; yet if they play with them, they soon leave them alone; there is nothing the child can add to their inflexible perfection. Mechanical tricks amuse grown-ups: they astonish children, and often kill their imagination.

How then, are we to retain in the production the simplicity and humanity of Andersen's story?

The first character to appear on the stage is the Story-teller—Andersen himself. He has the idea of showing us a story instead of telling one—he is going to make it up as he goes along, and sometimes he may have to take part in it himself.

Let us imagine that he makes his first entrance in front of the house curtain which, at the end of his speech, will rise to reveal the garret. This set is made of low flats, and contains a door and a window through which presently the Snow Queen will make her entrance, bringing the forces of magic and evil into this homely atmosphere, for the garret, though poor, is warm and friendly. The space occupied by the garret set should be used for all the important scenes of the play: it is a sort of inner stage, framed by two side wings and a border, and may be concealed by runner curtains when required. There should be enough space left in front of these runner curtains for the connecting scenes along the road to be played fairly easily. The runners represent a winter landscape, and will remain the same throughout the performance, though the side wings can be reversed to suggest different places and seasons.

The sets to be equipped on the inner stage should be simple enough to allow the changes to be carried out while the action takes place in front of the runners or during the interval, which comes after the scene in the King's Palace.

I believe that if one plans the scenery on this principle, the second part of the play can also run without a break until the departure of the children from the Far North, provided that the essential piece of scenery for the Snow Queen's Palace is set during the interval, and the robbers' tent attached to it. I consider this essential piece to be the throne where Kay will sit, which should be solidly built in such a way that it can revolve upon itself, to become in the following scene the great block of ice through which the children have to pass before escaping from the domain of the magic queen. A few masking curtains and a few mobile stalagmites of varying heights will be enough to complete the illusion; lighting, music and sound effects will do the rest for this important section of Gerda's adventure.

After as short a pause as possible, during which exciting and hopeful music will keep us from becoming impatient, we find ourselves in front of the runners again at the cross-roads, on the way to the south. The side wings now represent a rainy spring, free from the ice and snow of the far north. During this front scene, the garret is being set behind the runners, so that finally we are back once more in the warm familiar atmosphere created by Granny, free from the evil spells which have after all failed to gain the heart of Kay. So the Storyteller's improvised tale comes to a happy ending.

I realise only too well that this simplicity calls for great ingenuity and a good deal of taste, and that it cannot be attained at the first attempt. One must proceed with patience, discarding anything which is false or cumbersome. The important thing to remember is that the play as a whole should retain the character of a fairy story, and that only the garret set should give us an impression of familiar reality. The rest belongs to the realm of poetic fantasy.

The same may be said of the costumes. The characters fall into two groups: those of the real world, the Storyteller, the Grandmother, Gerda and Kay; and those of the imaginary world, in fact all the others, from the Chancellor to the animals.

The real people are dressed as our grandparents were—as we imagine them from pictures, photographs and daguerrotypes of the Victorian age.

The costumes for the imaginary characters are also derived from the same period; they show a certain social standing, and the Chancellor, the King, the Prince and the Princess are all dressed to give a general suggestion of the Victorian era, whose quaint and gracious style seems to us to suit the play very well. It is a northern Victorian style—clean, neat, a little prim, their hair is blond and their cheeks are glowing with the cold. The robbers are well muffled up in furs and skins, their heads covered. Nor should the animals be treated too seriously: the ravens are pompous and sentimental, the reindeer is tender, timid, faltering, affected, the bears are massive and lonely, the birds rapacious and fearful. All these characteristics should be marked and wittily exaggerated.

What more is there to say? It is always difficult to make a play from a book which has had no thought for the limitations of the stage. The task is made considerably harder when part of the book is fantasy, for fantasy knows no limits. The Snow Queen flies through the air, passes through the thickest of walls with a natural ease—and children like to see the impossible happen before their very eyes. But they want to be convinced and to believe in the illusion without understanding how it has been created. The strange thing is that they know there is a secret, a trick, and will ask innumerable questions to find out what it is, though their curiosity only increases their delight in accepting the impossible. We must not disappoint either their innocence or their sense of realism.

THE SNOW QUEEN

PART ONE

PROLOGUE

As the house curtain goes up we hear an impudent little tune. Enter in front of scene-curtain the STORYTELLER. *He is so absorbed in what his feet are doing that he does not notice the audience. He is trying to do a little dance to fit the tune.*

STORYTELLER (*out loud to himself as he dances*):

Snip! Snap! Snooper!
Pooper, bazalooper!
Snip! Snap! Snooper!
Crippety! Crappity—Ugh! (*As he fails to get the right step.*)
(*He snaps his fingers and begins again.*)
Snip! Snap! Snooper!
Pooper, bazalooper. (*Quickening.*)
Snip-snap-snooper—
Crippetycrappity—BOOM! (*He succeeds with his feet.*)
(*He hears the audience and slowly turns.*)

Oooh! People! . . . Thin ones. . . . Fat ones. . . . Old ones. . . . Young ones—short ones, tall ones, and some in between. (*Looks at them.*) You there, you go to school, eh? And you, huh, you, you are a teacher. And you are a mother and cook for your children. —And you are a busman.—And you an engineer. When you think of all the people in the world, and everyone doing something too, what a lot of doing it all adds up to! You see, I've also got a job; they call me Mr. Storyteller. I'm important too—for without storytellers there would be no good stories—good stories! Ah! (*Settling down.*) Now I'm going to tell you one about a clever boy called Kay and the Snow Queen, and how they go to her great Ice Palace in the snow, far, far, far . . . Oh, it's a lovely story! Magic roses, fights, robbers. . . . Do you know I know all the stories in the world? (*Suddenly.*) Do you see this sword? (*Humming and making a few steps with sword drawn.*) Snip! Snap! Snooper! I hope we'll run the villain through and let his wicked blood gush through the palace dungeons! Do you know, if I were to tell you a hundred stories a day for a hundred days, I would still have hundreds to tell you! But this one especially! Do you see this gun? You want to hear my story, don't you? Ah! I'll tell you what I'll do: I'll do more than just tell it to you—I'll show you the story as a play! Here! Listen! (*Confidentially*).

Behind that curtain sits a girl—Gerda and her friend, a boy—Kay. It's winter when the story begins. . . . Yes, I know how it begins, but I don't know how it's all going to end; for I haven't invented the end yet. I'll have to make it up as I go. I may even have to take part in it myself, if Kay and Gerda get into trouble. Anyway! Here we go! The Story of The Snow Queen! Sh! (*Sound of hammering is heard behind the curtain.*) I think I hear Kay mending his sledge . . . and . . . yes! There it is now— the organ-grinder's tune as he plays down in the cold streets below. . . . (*Music of barrel-organ.*) It's Gerda's favourite tune . . . and Granny's too. Sh. . . . !

With his fingers to his lips the STORYTELLER *opens the curtain as he goes off.*

GRANNY'S GARRET

A poor neat little garret. There is a large window through which we see snow-covered roofs and gables and a church steeple in the distance. It is towards evening and getting dark. A table with a lamp. A bench near it. A stove. Not far from it Granny's armchair. On the opposite side of the stage a chest and on it a rose-tree which is in full bloom though it is winter.

The organ-grinder is heard playing down in the courtyard.

GERDA, *a girl of about twelve years of age, sits in the armchair doing some needlework.* KAY, *a boy, is sitting on the floor repairing his sledge.*

GERDA (*after a silence*):   Listen, Kay!

KAY: The old organ-grinder!

GERDA: His music sounds quite muffled today—like cottonwool.

KAY: It's the snow.

(GERDA *stands at the window and looks down into the street.*)

GERDA: I can see the organ-grinder now: like a little black smudge in the snow.

KAY (*busy with sledge*):   Is he stamping his feet?

GERDA: Yes. How did you know?

KAY: Oh, he always does it. I used to think that he was doing a dance to the tune.

GERDA: He must be very cold down there.

KAY: He'll soon be home. (*Getting up.*) See, it's getting dark now.

(*Music stops.*)

3

GERDA: He's stopped.

KAY (*at window*):   There he goes.

GERDA: It's difficult pushing his way through the snow.

KAY: It's easy in the middle where the horses are dashing along.   Ah! Soon my sledge will be ready to go dashing along behind them. (*Going to sledge again.*)

GERDA (*still looking out of window*):   Snow is falling again. It dizzies me—watching snowflakes fall—like feathers.

KAY: I read in a book that they were frozen rain. (*Busy at sledge.*)

(*The music of the organ-grinder's tune comes back as* GERDA *begins to sing.*)

GERDA: Now the frost grips all the earth,
                    The birds begin to cry
                    Tears which fall
                    And freeze till all
                    As snowflakes fill the sky.

          (KAY *joins in humming during the song.*)
                    So all the snowflakes
                    Are tears that are silently
                    Gliding by . . .
                    For unless
                    God's sun will bless
                    Our earth, the birds will die.

(*The music fades out.* KAY *still hums it, then stops abruptly.*)

KAY: Listen, Gerda!

GERDA: What is it?

KAY: Sh! (*Silence.*) The stairs are squeaking . . . aren't they?

GERDA: Yes! Granny's coming!

          (*Steps offstage.* GERDA *runs to lay the table.*)

KAY (*running to the stove*):   Hoi! Granny, hurry up!

4

GERDA: Don't, Kay! Don't hurry her, she is old and there are so many stairs.

KAY: She can't hear me anyway. She is too far down. H'i, h'i, Granny! Hurry up!

GERDA: H'i, h'i, Granny! Be quick!

KAY: The kettle is singing! (*He takes the kettle from the stove.*)

GERDA (*running to prepare the tea*): . . . Singing . . . singing . . .

KAY (*astonished*): Stop! She's already wiping her shoes on the mat. . . . She was quick!

GERDA: Yes. . . . (*There is a knock at the door.*) Why did she knock?

KAY: Haha! To frighten us! (GERDA *giggles.*) Quiet! Let's frighten her. Don't answer.

(*Again there is knocking at the door. The children giggle. The knocking becomes louder.*)

GERDA (*whispering*): Let's hide.

KAY: Yes, let's.

(GERDA *and* KAY *hide underneath the table and behind the armchair. The door opens, in comes a tall* MAN *dressed in grey. He looks around. Silence.*)

GERDA: Miaow! Miaow!

KAY: Bow-wow!

(*The* MAN *jumps in surprise. Suddenly the two children rush out.*)

KAY AND GERDA: Ha! Ha! Granny! . . . Oh! (*They stare at the* MAN, *then at each other.*)

MAN: Ill-bred brats!

KAY: We are not ill-bred brats.

MAN: Silence! (*He turns on* KAY *and sees the roses.*) Ah! Stand aside. The roses! (*He moves towards them.*)

GERDA (*in frightened whispers to* KAY): What does he want with our roses?

KAY: How should I know?

MAN: Hm! They are real live ones . . . undoubtedly! For they have (a) the sickly scent of such plants, (b) their disgusting softness, and (c) their gaudy, girlish colour. Pooh! (*He breathes on them.*)

GERDA: Who can he be? He makes me shiver.

KAY: Me too. The room has got colder.

GERDA: And the kettle has stopped singing.

KAY: See! He's breathing on our roses.

GERDA: He's a magician.

MAN (*as though in anger at the roses*): Pah! (*He turns suddenly on the two children; they back away.*)

KAY (*bravely*): Who are you? What do you want? (*Panicky, as* MAN *advances.*)

MAN: It is only ill-bred brats who are—(*Poking him with stick*)—(a) inquisitive, (b) forward, and (c) noisy. Well brought-up children are (a) uninquisitive, (b) modest, and (c) SILENT! Hah! (*He breathes on them and* GERDA *screams. There is the sound of someone running up the stair and* GRANNY'S *voice calling.*)

GRANNY (*off*): Children! What are you doing! I'm coming! (*Sound of knocking boots on wall.*) I'm getting the snow off my feet! Well!

(GRANNY *comes in but does not notice* MAN.)

Did I leave you too long? I hope you didn't let the stove go out, Kay?—What's the matter with you? (*She follows the eyes of the children who are staring at the* MAN.) Oh!

MAN (*coming forward*): Good evening. . . .

GRANNY: Good evening . . . eh. . . . I'm afraid I don't know the gentleman's name.

MAN: Just call me 'Chancellor' . . .

GRANNY: Oh! Won't you sit down . . . Mr. . . . Chancellor. Gerda, get the Chancellor a seat by the fire.

MAN: Fires don't agree with me; and I did not come here to sit and gossip. . . .

GRANNY: Then I hope you don't mind if I do. I've been on my feet working all day.

MAN: You may sit. (*Imperiously.*) I have come here today on behalf of a powerful lady. She has a demand to make of you.

GRANNY: Oh! If it's to do charring or any outside work, sir, I don't know that I could fit it in. But if it's mending or washing that I could do here in the evening, I might. Let me see . . . Thursdays I . . .

MAN: Fiddlesticks! This lady does not want anything like that.

GRANNY: Some baking, perhaps?

GERDA: Granny bakes wonderful cakes!

KAY: Scrumptious ones!

MAN: Fiddlesticks! Fiddlesticks! She doesn't want your cakes, or your work. She simply wants that rose-tree. (*Pointing to it.*)

GERDA: The rose-tree!

GRANNY: Oh! We can't part with our rose-tree, sir.

MAN: You *must*! The lady I speak of wants it so much that she is prepared to reward you handsomely.

GRANNY: Does she love roses so much?

MAN: She hates them. (*They are taken aback.*) She loathes them and especially those which flower in winter.

GRANNY: But if she doesn't like them what does she want them for?

7

MAN (*looking hatefully at the roses as if at a human enemy*):   To bury them deep under the ice.

GERDA: Granny!

GRANNY: Hush!

MAN: Ask your price or anything in exchange. *Anything* —I will consider it.

GRANNY: Our roses are not for sale, sir.

KAY: Good old Granny!

MAN: Fiddlesticks! (*To* KAY.) And as for *you*! What a pity your Granny won't part with them; for in exchange I could have given you such wonderful ice-crystals.

KAY: Crystals. Oh!

MAN: . . . A collection of ice-crystals each one of which is a different design. Some with a million sides, yet so small that all you see is a glitter, and some as big as your head.

KAY: As big as my head? A crystal?

GRANNY: Mr. Chancellor, I have told you—we cannot part with our rose-tree. It is a very special one. The Storyteller has said that it will flower all the time—even in winter—as long as we are happy together here.

CHANCELLOR: And you refuse to part with it?

GRANNY: Yes.

CHANCELLOR: Well! We will see! So long as you are all happy together, eh? You will soon realise that you have been a very foolish old woman.

KAY: Don't talk to my Granny that way!

CHANCELLOR: She is just a stubborn old goat.

KAY: You . . . ! You are a wicked old man!

GRANNY: Kay, stop that!

CHANCELLOR: Hahaa! We shall *freeze* you, my boy. We shall freeze you.

GERDA: We won't let you! Go away!

8

CHANCELLOR: We shall see! Good-day, you stupid old woman.

KAY: Oh! . . . Everybody! . . . Just everybody . . . loves our Granny and you . . . you . . . just growl at her, you . . . you . . .

GRANNY (*restraining him*): Kay!

KAY: You iceberg!

CHANCELLOR: Haha! We shall see what will happen to you now. I shall go to the lady who sent me—I shall go to the Queen! (*Reaching for his hat.*) You know which Queen!

(*They are all rather alarmed at the* CHANCELLOR'S *last statement. The* STORYTELLER, *who has been coming up the stairs, can now be heard singing.*)

STORYTELLER (*off*): . . . Crippety! Crappity. . . . Boom!

(*The* STORYTELLER *and the* CHANCELLOR *collide in the doorway.*)

CHANCELLOR: Fool!

(*The* CHANCELLOR *goes.*)

STORYTELLER: Crippety! What an icicle! (*He comes forward into the room.*) Snip! Snap' Snooper! Ah! What's the matter? Has that old snowdrift upset you? (*Silence.*) Eh? Come now.

GERDA: Oh, Mr. Storyteller—he wanted to take our roses away.

STORYTELLER: Ah! (*Turns to rose-tree.*) Well, he didn't get them anyway. (*He goes to the roses.*) I am glad he didn't. And so are they, aren't you, roses? What do you say? What did you say, little bud? That you always want to live here with Gerda and Kay and with Granny, who gives you a drink of water every day and sometimes gives Mr. Storyteller a drink of tea.

9

GRANNY: Haha! (*Laughing despite herself.*) I'm glad you've come to cheer us up. And there's the kettle singing again!

STORYTELLER: Ah! (*Crossing.*) What's that, kettle? What did you say? Fizzz! You're hisssssssssing angry? Why? At them letting you ssit and ssplutter—now! don't stutter —Oh! And if I come near you you'll sssssssssssssscald me! Oh!

GRANNY AND GERDA: Haha!

GRANNY: You'll burn your hand. Here's a kettle-holder.
(*They all laugh but* KAY.)

STORYTELLER: Hullo! What's the matter with you, Kay?

KAY: Oh nothing! Leave me alone.

STORYTELLER: Come now! Out with it.

KAY: Well. . . . It's that man . . . the Chancellor.

GRANNY: Oh, let's forget him. He's gone.

KAY: Yes, but he said he's gone to the Queen. What Queen would that be?

STORYTELLER: Ah! Judging from his icy looks I would say it must be the Snow Queen.

KAY: The Snow Queen!

STORYTELLER: Yes. She has hard-hearted messengers who go all over the world trying to freeze the heart of things and people.
(*There is a gust of wind and the window rattles.*)

GERDA: Oh! (*Jumping.*) Someone knocked at the window. (*Opening a half of the curtain.*)

GRANNY: It was only the snow; and the wind. Have your tea to warm you.
(*They sit to tea round the stove.*)

STORYTELLER: The Snow Queen couldn't do much damage here. All our hearts are too warm, and with Granny's tea she couldn't freeze us at all. But you are too hot, cup!

GERDA: If she came we'd sit her up on the stove and she would melt away. Ha! ha!

KAY: Where does she live?

STORYTELLER: Oh, in the Summer she lives far far away on the furthest north point of the Earth. But in the Winter she comes sweeping down to our land, gliding on a big black cloud. And then, at night while we are asleep, she'll glide through the streets silently. She sometimes looks through a window and when we get up in the cold morning we find the whole of the window glass frosted with flowers.

(*Gust of wind and window rattles.*)

GERDA: Look! The frost-flowers in the window! Does that mean that she was here?

STORYTELLER: Perhaps she just looked in and went away.

GERDA: I wish I could have seen her.

KAY: Have *you* ever seen the Snow Queen?

STORYTELLER: Yes, I have seen her—once.

GERDA: Oh, tell me!

STORYTELLER: Well, once—— Oh! before you were born, I . . . but I mustn't tell you a story now or Granny might scold me for keeping you from your home-lessons.

KAY: Go on! Granny's dozing off by the fire, sh!

GERDA (*whispering*): And we've done most of our lessons.

STORYTELLER (*whispering*): History?

KAY AND GERDA: Yes, yes.

STORYTELLER (*whispering*): Writing?

KAY AND GERDA: Yes, yes.

STORYTELLER (*whispering*): Sums? (*Normal voice.*) Ah! She's snoring now. She deserves her sleep, and you deserve a story. Now . . . ! (*Settling to it professionally.*) One night, long, long ago a strange thing happened to

me. At that time my mother—just like Granny—went
out to work for other ladies all day. But she wasn't so
strong as Granny and like me her hands were clumsy; so
it would often occur that she didn't get home till very
late. Now one evening I was waiting patiently. It was
later than she'd ever been and it was winter. The wind
was blowing like—well, like tonight . . . a North wind.
Well, I waited and I waited, but presently the candle
burnt right down and went out. Then I got frightened.
The old street lamp outside our window creaked and
swung about in the wind; and as it swung to and fro it
sent weird shadows scampering across the floor and up
and down the walls of the room. I snatched my cap and
scarf and ran out of the house, slamming the door. It
wasn't so eerie waiting out in the street. It was dead
quiet. I pushed aside some dry snow and sat on the step.
Then—suddenly—the wind whipped dry snow off the
street, and the roofs and the railings and the gate. And
it all whirled round and round in the wind till I could
hardly see for snow. *Then it happened——* Inside the
whirling snow a very beautiful white shape grew, like the
hugest snowflake you ever saw, and as the wind blew
faster and snowflakes flew around and around it grew and
grew and grew and grew till . . .

(*A great gust of wind and at the same time his hand sweeps the
lamp off the table and there is a blackout.*)

GRANNY (*crying out*):   Children!

STORYTELLER: It was my clumsy hands again! I'll light the
lamp.

(*He does so; but the light is different now. It flickers strangely
and in the light there stands a beautiful* WOMAN *in white,
with blue hair and glittering diamonds in it.*)

ALL: Oh!

STORYTELLER: It's the . . . (*Before he can say more the* WOMAN *waves her hand and he seems unable to speak.*)

WOMAN: I knocked, but perhaps I was not heard?

KAY: Granny said it . . . was only the snow.

WOMAN: Did I frighten you?

KAY (*frightened*): Oh no—not a bit, really!

WOMAN: I am glad. I like a brave boy. (*To others.*) Good evening to you all.

GRANNY: Good evening . . . madam. Will you . . . sit down?

WOMAN: I thank you, no.

GRANNY: Oh it's so cold! Let me close the window. (*She closes it.*)

WOMAN: The cold does not worry me; but it might damage the . . . roses. (*Moving to them.*)

GRANNY: Oh! (*Not sure.*) Perhaps a cup of tea would . . .

WOMAN: . . . Tea! I hate anything hot. Thank you. So you are all happy together here. . . . Hm. . . . But I am afraid I shall have to disturb you. The girl is your granddaughter?

GRANNY: Yes, madam.

WOMAN (*turning to* KAY): And *you*—are you her brother?

KAY: A friend.

WOMAN: Ah! A foster-child!

KAY: I am not a foster-child.

GRANNY: Of course not, dear. (*Aside to* WOMAN.) It's true he is not my grandson. When his parents died he had no one in the world; so I gave him a home. But now he is just one of my children.

WOMAN: Hm. . . . But you are very old.

KAY: Granny isn't old at all! . . . Are you?

GRANNY: Well . . .

WOMAN (*to* GRANNY):   And you might grow ill.

GERDA: Granny won't grow ill!

WOMAN (*to* GRANNY):   You might . . . die.

GERDA AND KAY: She can't die!

WOMAN: Silence! (*Angrily and then calmly.*) I am used to silence when I speak; *and what I say is true.* (*To* GRANNY.) *Is it not?* (GRANNY *is troubled and does not answer.*) And so I shall take the boy with me.

KAY: What!

WOMAN: I am a Queen. My palace is very, very large and very lonely for me. (*To* KAY.) You will stay with me. (*To* GRANNY.) I will make the boy my son, so he shall be a prince. Would you stand in his way?

GERDA: Granny, Granny, don't give him away! He can work if it's hard for you; deliver newspapers, chop wood, or clear snow away. . . .

KAY (*to* GERDA):   I can speak for myself.

GERDA (*continuing*):   Granny, don't give him away!
                (*Calming gesture from* GRANNY.)

KAY: Granny, you don't want me to go away, do you?

GRANNY: I never want to part with you!

KAY (*to* QUEEN):   There! You see. I can't come.

QUEEN: There is no need to hurry. Think about it, Kay. You will live in a beautiful palace and there you will have everything. . . .

KAY: . . . But I won't have Granny and Gerda. So I won't come!

STORYTELLER: Good boy!

QUEEN: Silence! (*She again waves her hand over the* STORYTELLER.)

GRANNY: I am sorry . . . madam. I can't let you have

him; even if he is naughty at times. Yes—he makes me sad and angry, now and then. But more often he makes me happy. He is my boy and he shall stay with me.

GERDA: Yes.

QUEEN: Very well. As you will. Stay here . . . Kay; if you like it so much—if you don't wish to become a prince. Good-bye. Good-bye. (*Smiling.*) Don't you want to kiss me good-bye?

KAY: No, I don't.

QUEEN: So you are afraid of me—and I thought you were a brave boy.

KAY: I'm not afraid of anything!

QUEEN: Not *anything*? Then—kiss me good-bye.
(KAY *moves forward.*)

GERDA: Don't, Kay! . . .

KAY: Good-bye!

QUEEN: Good-bye! (*She kisses him.*)
(*The wind moans.*)
Soon we shall meet again . . . Kay.
(*Light flickers and dies for a moment. Wind. . . . When the light returns the* QUEEN *has gone.*)

STORYTELLER: It was the Snow Queen; I tried to warn you.

GERDA: The Snow Queen!

GRANNY: Have done with your stories! (*Angrily.*) Kay!
(KAY *has wandered over to the rose-tree.*)

KAY: Look. The roses are dead. (*To* STORYTELLER.) You said they'd never die. See! (*He picks a rose and throws it on the floor.*)

GERDA: Kay!

GRANNY: The rose-tree withered!—Oh! (*She runs to it.*) Oh! How sad!

KAY (*aping her*): 'How sad!' Granny waddles like a goose when she runs.

GERDA: Kay! Kay!

KAY: Kay! Kay! Well, it's true, isn't it! (*He demonstrates how* GRANNY *runs.*)

GRANNY: Kay!

KAY: Well, what are you staring at? You've seen me before. . . . Haven't you?

GRANNY: What's come over you? I don't recognise you.

KAY: Oh! You're getting old and shortsighted that's all!

GERDA: Kay, how can you say such a thing!

KAY (*imitating her*): 'How can you say such a thing!' How can I say such a thing? Because it's true, and because I'm fed up with this garret and you two with your soppy notions—that's why! (*He turns away to the window.*)

GERDA (*low voice*): Kay!

(*A long silence.*)

STORYTELLER: Yes—it was the Snow Queen. . . .

GERDA: But . . . why didn't you tell us at first?

STORYTELLER: I couldn't. . . . She waved her hand at me, and it was as if I were turned to ice. . . .

KAY: Ice—fiddlesticks!

GERDA: Kay! You sound like the Chancellor. . . .

KAY: I'm glad. He's sensible—not soft like you.

GERDA (*speechless*): Oh!

GRANNY: Children, to bed! It's late. You are beginning to quarrel. Do you hear? At once; wash—and to bed!

GERDA (*crying*): Granny . . . I want to know what is wrong with him.

KAY: 'Aehhhhh!' How ugly you are when you cry! 'Aehh.'

16

STORYTELLER (*leading* GERDA *to the bedroom door*): Nothing! Kay must sleep it off. That's all.

KAY: 'Aehhhh!'

STORYTELLER: Kay!! You are both going to bed now. We'll say good-night to you later.

(*The children go off.*)

GRANNY (*aghast*): But . . . what has come over the boy?

STORYTELLER: Come, come, don't worry. Here, first, sit down—and then, here, have a cup of tea.—You see (*sits down*)—when I met the Snow Queen she asked me to kiss her too—but I did not, I ran away. And mother said to me afterwards that this was the right thing to do. . . . If the Snow Queen kisses you, your heart turns to ice. . . . (*Low.*) Now our little Kay has a heart of ice. . . .

GRANNY: But that is not possible! No. No. You'll see. Tomorrow he'll wake up as good and as gay as ever.

STORYTELLER: Perhaps. But suppose he does not? What then? What's to be done? (*They sit silently.*) No, Snow Queen, I am not going to let you have the little boy. (*Wind grows stronger.*) I am not afraid of you! Whistle, howl, sing, shake the window, I shall find out how to deal with you, Snow Queen—I shall!—Though I don't know yet . . . I don't know yet. . . .

(*The* SNOW QUEEN'S *voice is heard calling outside:*)

QUEEN (*in the distance*): Kay! . . .

(*Neither* GRANNY *nor the* STORYTELLER *hear the call. But the door of the children's room opens, and out comes* KAY, *walking on tiptoe, his coat over his arm, and listening attentively. He reaches the door, but before he can slip out, there is another call, this time nearer.*)

(*Off stage*): Kay! . . .

(KAY *looks towards the window . . . the* SNOW QUEEN *appears*)

17   C

in the frame. KAY climbs up to the sill.—The SNOW QUEEN smiles at him and puts one of her arms around him so that he is almost entirely covered by her long sleeve.)
Come!

Only now the STORYTELLER and GRANNY look up. They see what is happening and utter an inarticulate 'Kay!' . . . But the SNOW QUEEN and KAY turn to fly away.

BLACKOUT

SCENE 2

ON THE ROAD TO THE NORTH

GERDA *comes in, tramping wearily and carrying a small bundle. She is humming the organ-grinder's tune.*

GERDA: Everywhere I go I find the roads the same and the people strange. . . . Oh! (*Stopping.*) I wonder how many days, how many weeks, how many months I have travelled now? The snow had just gone when I left home. Then came the Spring and the flowers, and the sun got hotter and hotter, till the Summer came and the dust. The leaves are falling about me now, so it must be Autumn and . . . Oh! (*Realising it.*) It will soon be Winter again and I still have not found Kay. Must I search all through the cold Winter too? (*She weeps a little and sits.*) Now I know what it is to be really alone. All alone! (*Looking round, sighs.*)

(*Suddenly a raven—*KARL—*appears. She does not see him and he does not see her. He crows to himself.*)

KARL: Kra!—k a!

(GERDA *screams and jumps up. At her scream* KARL *screeches and flaps a good foot into the air. They both stand apart, facing and unsure of each other.*)

GERDA (*timidly*): Good . . . afternoon . . . Mr. . . . Raven.

KARL (*timidly*): Good . . . afternoon . . . madam . . . or miss.

(*Silence as they eye each other.*)

You aren't going to grasp for a branch and thrash me?

GERDA: Why, no, sir.

KARL: Nor cast a sharp stone at my back?

GERDA: No, sir.

KARL: Nor your parcel?

GERDA: Oh no, sir.

KARL: Ah! (*Relieved.*) Grand! Grand! You are marvellously well brought-up! Maaarvellously! Don't I talk grandly?

GERDA: You do indeed.

KARL: Hahaha! Passing my young days in the castle park —I learned the jargon of the court. I am half a court raven. But Klara is a court raven in fact!

GERDA: Klara? But who is that?

KARL: Klara is my bride to be. She gets her nourishment from the royal larder, real royal garbage, you understand?

GERDA: Yes, I see, sir.

KARL: You aren't from these parts—or are you?

GERDA (*sighing*): No, sir, I come from very far away.

KARL: Far parts—far parts—I took it for granted.—Is that why you are so downhearted?

GERDA: No, it's because I can't find my friend whom I am looking for—everywhere—a boy.

KARL: A lad? Ah! Can I help you? I'm a past master in helping!

GERDA: Thank you. Oh, if you only could. You see, we lived together so happily—he and Granny and I. But one day, last winter, the Snow Queen came and fetched him —and he has never been seen again. The name of the boy is . . .

KARL (*quickly*): Kay?

GERDA: How do you know?

KARL: And you are Gerda?

GERDA: Yes, I am called Gerda. But how . . . ?

KARL: Haha! Our aunt, the magpie, a ghastly gossip, knows all that passes in the far world!

GERDA: Then you . . . you know where Kay is? Answer me! Quick!

KARL: Kra-ra! Kra-ra!—For forty days we asked and guessed, discussed and examined the facts . . .

GERDA: And?

KARL: . . . tried to establish, to learn, to discover where he had vanished to . . .

GERDA: And?

KARL: . . . to detect his moves, to track them, to check them . . .

GERDA: And?

KARL: . . . to . . . to . . . to . . .

GERDA: And?

KARL: Not a chance of a glance!

GERDA (*disappointed*): Oh . . . !

KARL: Hark!

GERDA: What's the matter?

KARL: Hark! Hark! That's Klara! That charming flapping of her wings. Grand!

(*A second raven appears.*)

Darling Klara!

KLARA: Darling Karl!

KARL: How are you, Klara?

KLARA: How are you, Karl?

KARL: Marvellous!

KLARA: I have vastly interesting news. You'll gasp, Karl.

KARL: But I do! (*He opens his beak wide.*)

KLARA: Not too far apart! Not too far! It is crude and rude! (*She adjusts his beak.*) There! (*Continuing.*) Imagine, Karl, imagine: Kay . . .

GERDA AND KARL: Kay?

KLARA: I have news of Kay. Stand there, Karl, while I impart it, that I can mark how startled you are. Imagine, Karl—Kay's in the castle!

GERDA: What?—You're sure? What castle?

KLARA (*jumps round*):   Ahh, who's that?

KARL: Don't be alarmed, Klara. That's Gerda.

KLARA: Gerda? What marvels! (*She curtsies ceremoniously.*) How are you, Gerda?

GERDA: Do tell me, what castle? How is Kay? Who found him?

(*The* RAVENS *speak to each other excitedly in the ravens' language then they come to* GERDA.)

KARL AND KLARA (*both trying to talk at once*):   Actually . . . !
(*They stop and bow to each other.*)

KLARA: After you Karl! (*Looking daggers at him.*)

KARL (*conciliatory*):   No. After you, Klara, daaarling!

KLARA (*beginning again*):   One week past, little Christina . . .

KARL: . . . The Princess . . .

KLARA: The *Princess*, went to her father . . .

KARL: The King . . .

KLARA (*quickly*):   . . . The Princess went to the King; *and* she said to her dear *Papa*, 'Papa'—— (*Stops. To* KARL.) What did she say?

KARL: 'I'm bored.'

KLARA: 'I'm bored, *Papa*,' she said, 'and if I can't get married, I'd rather be dead.'

BOTH: That's what she said.

GERDA: But why do you tell me this?

BOTH: *Aaaaaah!* Wait!

KARL: After you, Klara!

KLARA: After you, Karl!

KARL: Well, Princess Christina said to her *dad*, I shan't
let you *ma*rry me to a *lad* who just says 'Yes' to all I
say . . .

KLARA: . . . Because that's why I'm bored, that's why I'm
sad. Everyone's too *good*. I want some *lad* who is *brave*
enough to be *bad*—to me.

KARL: So the King ordered every country *lad* to come to
the castle and see who *had* no *fear* of Christina . . .

KLARA: . . . and her *dad*; and they were all afraid except
one *lad* . . .

GERDA: Kay?

BOTH: Kay! That's the *lad*!

KLARA: He just *lau*ghed and chatted unabashed.

GERDA: That would be Kay! He's not afraid of anyone.

KLARA: He chaffed the Princess . . .

KARL: . . . and her *dad*. And the Princess said, 'That's the
lad!' And they were married; and her *dad* . . .

KLARA: His Majesty the King . . .

KARL: . . . Her *dad* gave them *half* of his kingdom.

KLARA: *An*d a marvellous garden-party!

BOTH: Kra-kra!

GERDA: But are you quite certain that it is Kay?

KARL: Absolutely!

KLARA: *Ac*tually . . . this afternoon I heard Christina say
—to the Prince, 'Come here, *Kay*!'

KARL: *An*d he said, 'The Snow Queen has kidnapped
me!'

GERDA: I must go to the castle . . . right away.

BOTH: Kra!-kra!

KLARA: The roads are ghastly. We will fly. On my back!
I will carry Gerda to the castle.

KARL: Pardon me. I am stronger. I will carry Gerda.

KLARA (*sharply*): Wait till you're *as*ked for gallantry!
(KARL *is hurt.*) Karl! Let's both carry Gerda.
(GERDA *mounts on her back.*)
KARL: Kra! kra!
KLARA: Now, to the castle!
BOTH: Kra! Kra! Kra! Kra!

KARL, KLARA *and* GERDA *start to flap off as the light fades out.*

When the light returns the stage is empty. A silent man, the CHANCELLOR, *wrapped up to his nose in a fur coat, enters —and crosses the stage—apparently following* GERDA. *He does not notice another man, the* STORYTELLER, *who follows him at a safe distance.*

BLACKOUT

SCENE 3

IN THE KING'S CASTLE

The curtain opens in the dark. A hall in the Royal Palace—a somewhat sombre place in gloomy light. Out of the vaulted room there leads in the background an apparently endless gallery. Across the middle of the floor goes a chalk line, very noticeable in the half darkness, dividing the hall and the gallery into two exactly equal parts, the right one darker and more sinister than the left.

The stage is empty. As a clock strikes eleven, a MAN IN GREY *appears, who silently moves along the line and looks towards the left . . . Suddenly he seems to notice something and withdraws in silence . . .*

A side door opens L. *very silently, and* KLARA *peeps into the room. Then she hops in.*

KLARA (*whispering*):   Karl!

KARL (*off stage, whispering*):   Klara!

KLARA: Karl! (*Reprimanding.*) Be a *man*! Be a *man*!

KARL (*entering, looking around*):   Empty—all empty . . .

KLARA (*to* GERDA):   Beware! Beware!

KARL: Keep to this half of the hall!

KLARA: Beware the line!

KARL: Beware! Beware!

GERDA: But, what's the meaning of this line?

KLARA: When His Majesty gave Christina and Kay half of his kingdom they got half of the castle too. This line cuts right through the heart of the kingdom. This half is Christina's. That's her father's.

KARL: Better beware of the father's half.

GERDA: What a gloomy place!

KLARA: Beware! Beware! The castle is dark and damp and vast, with passages which for centuries past no one has entered.

KARL: Rats live there.

KLARA: And nasty, maggoty, ghastly things.

KARL: And ghosts!—ghosts of the past.

KLARA: And dusty curtains harbour bats!

GERDA: Ugh!!!

KLARA: And sometimes in the stagnant air . . .

KARL AND KLARA: . . . shrieks are heard! Brrrrrrrrrrrr!

GERDA: And this (*looking round*) is where Kay lives?
  (*Both* RAVENS *nod silently and impressively. The silence is broken by a weird noise.*)

KARL (*jumping with fright*): Klara!—What's that?
                  (*Noise again.*)

KLARA: I can't quite grasp, but . . .

GERDA: Ssh! Listen!
              (*Noise again, approaching.*)

KARL (*terrified*): Klara! Klara!

KLARA: What can it be?
              (*Noise nearer.*)

KARL: Let's not wait and see.

KLARA: Karl, you're scared!

KARL: No. But as a man it's my duty to protect you. Therefore I command you to run away to a safe place.
  (*He is about to run off first.*)

KLARA: Karl! After me!
              (*Noise approaching all the time.*)

GERDA (*stopping them both*): Stop! We mustn't run away now. It might be Kay! Let's hide here! Come! Quickly!
  (GERDA *bundles* KARL *and* KLARA *into hiding with her as the*

noise grows and the door L. *opens and in bursts a* HORSE *made up of two people,* CHRISTINA *riding on it.—A* LACKEY *accompanies them, carrying two candlesticks with burning candles and lighting the* HORSE'S *capricious progress. Followed by another* LACKEY *with cymbals and a third* LACKEY *with a trumpet.*)

PRINCESS (*like a circus-rider, urging the* HORSE):   Ho, ho!— More music! Louder! Quicker!

(*The noise becomes dreadful. The* HORSE *runs about, wilder and wilder, and the 'forelegs' seem to be rather unruly.*)
Stop that!

(CHRISTINA *is thrown off.*)

For shame! (*Furious, puts her crown straight.*) You don't know how to play! You frighten me!

(*The* HORSE *bursts out laughing, takes his head off, and out of the 'fore-legs' climbs a boy of about fourteen, laughing; he is the* PRINCE.)

PRINCE (*laughing*):   You wanted to marry somebody who wasn't afraid of you—I'm not.

PRINCESS: You are insolent!

PRINCE: But you like me—haha!

(LACKEYS *are still beating the cymbals and blowing the trumpet.*)

PRINCESS (*to the* LACKEYS):   Do stop that noise! (*They stop.*)

PRINCE: That's better. I'm tired of playing circuses. (*Seeing the hind legs standing miserably in a corner, carrying the fore-legs and the horse's head.*) And he's tired, too. Send the hind legs to bed.

PRINCESS: You can go.

LACKEYS: Good-night, your Royal Highnesses!

(*The* LACKEYS *go off—except the one who bears the candlesticks.*)

27

PRINCE: Good-night, old chap! (*Giving the 'hind legs' a friendly clap.*) Good-night, hind legs!

(*The 'hind legs' puts the head on for ease of carrying, but puts it by mistake back to front and so makes it impossible to see. He trips over something and falls out.* CHRISTINA *and* KLAUS *both laugh.*)

(*Tidying himself in front of a mirror.*) I'm sorry if I was too rough!

(*Sound of weeping from* GERDA *in hiding.*)

PRINCE: Oh! There's no need to be a cry-baby!

PRINCESS: I'm not a cry-baby!

(*More weeping off.*)

PRINCE: Well, you're crying all right!

(*More weeping off.*)

PRINCESS: I tell you, I'm not crying!

(*More weeping.*)

PRINCE (*turning angrily*):   Then if you're not crying who . . . ?

(*Stops as he hears weeping.*)

PRINCESS: Yes who? Who is crying?

(*As they both look to where it is coming from, the weeping* GERDA *comes out, followed by fearful* KLARA *and* KARL.)

GERDA (*tearfully*):   It is I! I . . . I . . . I'm sorry . . . but . . . oooo! (*She bursts into tears again.*)

KARL: Pardon! Pardon, Your Highnesses, but . . .

PRINCE: Quiet, you! (*Turning to* GERDA.) What are you crying for? And how did you get in?

KLARA AND KARL: Actually . . .

PRINCE: Stop chattering!

PRINCESS: Dear little girl, we won't hurt you. But why are you crying?

GERDA (*sobbing*):   I . . . I was behind the curtain . . . and . . . ooooooo! (*Tears again.*)

PRINCESS: You were behind the curtain and what then?

GERDA: ... Th ... there was a little hole in it ...

PRINCESS: Yes?

GERDA: ... I ... looked through it and ...

PRINCESS: ... and ...

GERDA: ... then I saw his (*pointing to* PRINCE)—his *face*!
Ooooool (*In tears.*)

PRINCESS (*enjoying this*):   And was that why you were crying?

GERDA (*swallowing hard*):   ... Yes.

(PRINCESS *laughs.*)

PRINCE: What's wrong with my face?

GERDA: Oh! Nothing, please. It is just because it isn't
Kay's face.

PRINCE: Of course not. It's my own face. And I am
Klaus.

GERDA: But the raven said he heard you, Princess, call
him ... (*Gesture.*) ... 'Kay'.

PRINCE AND PRINCESS (*looking at each other*):   Kay? (*To the
others.*) When?

KLARA: Actually, after lunch—this afternoon.

PRINCESS: Oh, that was when you told me the story of
Kay and Gerda.

PRINCE: Oh yes! And then we played that I was Kay.

PRINCESS: And I was Gerda.

GERDA (*sobbing*):   But ... I am Gerda.

PRINCE AND PRINCESS: You——? Gerda?

PRINCE: Now I see!

PRINCESS: It must have been a terrible disappointment.
Come, Gerda, come, little girl, don't cry! I'll give you
this ribbon. (*She wants to take off her sash.*)

PRINCE: Nonsense! That won't be any real help to her.
(*Low voice.*) Ask Gerda to stay.

PRINCESS: You are now our guest in the castle, Gerda.

GERDA (*drying tears*): Oh! Thank you, but I must go on.

PRINCE: To search for Kay?

GERDA: Yes, Prince . . .

PRINCE: 'Prince'—nonsense! Just call me Klaus.

PRINCESS: And me Christina.

GERDA: Thank you, Klaus, thank you, Christina.

RAVENS (*giggling, delighted*): Christina! Christina!

PRINCE (*to ravens*): Stop chattering! (*To* GERDA.) And where do you hope to find Kay?

GERDA: In the far, far north, perhaps . . . in the Snow Queen's land. . . .

PRINCE: But that's a long way . . . (*Pause.*) (*Suddenly.*) I know! We'll give Gerda the coach!

KARL: *Ra-ra!*

PRINCESS: And four black horses!

KLARA (*delighted*): *Ra-ra!*

GERDA (*embarrassed*): But . . .

PRINCE: And fur gloves—and a muff!

PRINCESS: And fur boots!

PRINCE: And a fur cap!

PRINCESS: And a fur coat!

GERDA: No, no, Christina, I can't accept that!

PRINCESS: Why not? I shan't miss it. I have four hundred and eighty-nine fur coats.

PRINCE: But first you must have a proper rest.

GERDA: Please, Klaus, please, Christina, don't make me go to bed first. I can sleep in the coach.

PRINCE: Alright. (*Impatiently.*) Ravens! Fly to the stables. Tell the grooms to harness four black horses to the coach! At once!

PRINCESS: The golden coach!

GERDA: Oh! At least not the *golden* coach, please!

PRINCESS: Don't argue! You'll look so much nicer in that one.

KLARA (*going*): A carriage! A carriage!

KARL: Black mares! Black mares! Black mares!

(KLARA *and* KARL *go.*)

PRINCE: Now let's fetch the fur coat!

PRINCESS: And the other things. You are not afraid to be left alone?

PRINCE: Of course not. (*To* GERDA.) Nobody can touch you on this side of the line.

GERDA: Thank you. I'll sit here. (*Pointing to a stool.*)

PRINCE: Fine. We'll be back soon.

(*They both go off quickly with one candlestick.*)

GERDA: Thank you, Christina. Thank you, Klaus. (*Sits down.*) How nice they are to me.—But this castle is really very strange . . . so old and damp and gloomy. And those ghosts . . . (*The clock starts striking again.*) One . . . I hope it's not midnight on top of everything . . . four . . . five . . . If the ghosts appeared . . . seven . . . I hope they will be back soon . . . eleven . . . twelve. (*Short silence.*) Midnight . . . Brrrr! But . . . but . . . somebody's coming. (*Slowly.*) If it's the ghost of Christina's great-great-great-grandfather, what shall I . . .

(*The* KING *enters.*)

Oh! (*Curtsies.*) G-good evening, great-great-great grandfather. . . .

KING (*fixing his eyes on her*): Hm? . . . Grandfather?

GERDA: Yes, sir . . . (*Seeing his angry eyes.*) I am sorry if I said anything wrong . . . I have never met a ghost before. . . .

KING: A ghost? I . . .?

GERDA: Yes ... and I don't quite know how to talk to a ghost.

KING: A ghost. ... Hm? ... You think I am ...

GERDA (*curtsies*): A great-great-great-grandfather of Christina.

KING (*staring at her*): Christina!—That hussy! Hm— Come here. Come here!

GERDA: Please excuse me ... but ...

KING: When I say 'Come', people obey!—Ghosts are not kept waiting.

GERDA (*takes a few steps towards line, then stops*): Klaus said I should not cross the line.

KING (*loudly*): And *I* say: come here.

(GERDA *moves nearer, then retires.*)

(*Impatiently, shouting.*) Enough of this nonsense! I am— no ghost.

GERDA: No ghost?

KING (*comes down the line, appears in the light*): I am the King—Princess Christina's father—the King!

GERDA: Oh—I am sorry, sir.

KING: 'Sir'! He who wears this ring is used to be addressed as 'Your Majesty.'

(*He stretches his hand over the line. He is wearing a large ring.*)

GERDA (*intimidated*): Yes, Your Majesty.

(*She approaches the line to look at the ring. The* KING *quickly catches her.*)

KING: Guards! Guards!

(*Trumpets offstage—secret doors open—guards enter as* GERDA *just succeeds to free herself and jumps into the light half of the Hall.*)

GERDA: Shame! Shame! You cheated, you—the King!

KING (*furious, to the* GUARDS): Well! . . . What are you standing around for listening? Off with you! (GUARDS *off.*) And you. Have you no sense of etiquette? What a way to talk to me—the King! . . . To scold me—in front of my soldiers! You have shamed me. You have no feelings.

GERDA: I have . . . but you wanted to trap me!

KING (*still angry*): No—not I! (*Then looking round anxiously; low voice.*) He did!

GERDA: He? Who?

KING (*low voice, irritated*): I shall tell you, if only you will come here.

(GERDA *shakes her head. Moves away from line.*)

(*Shouting.*) I can't shout it across the whole room! Be seated. (*Gesture.*)

GERDA (*taking her stool to the line, sitting down*): I'll sit down on *this* side.

KING (*grumbling*): You are insolent! Disobedient! And . . . and—look at me—having to carry my own seat! I the King!

(*Then grumbling and with a sigh goes to fetch another stool, sits down on his side of the line. They begin a conversation in whispers and very confidentially.*)

More and more indignity! You see, the Chancellor wants me——

GERDA: The Chancellor? Oh! Where is he?

KING: Oh, he is somewhere in the castle. He wants me to——

GERDA (*turning round*): In this castle? How does he know that I am here?

KING: Oh, he has eyes everywhere. But what I am telling you is that he wants me to put you into a dungeon. You will let me, won't you? Eh?

33   D

GERDA (*slightly withdrawing from* KING): Put me into a dungeon?

KING: It's not my idea. I'd let you go.

GERDA: But . . . you are the King—can't you protect me from him?

KING: No, I can't!

GERDA: But why? You are not scared of him, are you?

KING (*low voice*): No—not of him—but of *her*.

GERDA: Whom?

KING: The Snow Queen.

GERDA: Is she here too?

KING: No, no. She lives in her land to the north, which borders on my Kingdom. She is very powerful and she might come to invade my country, if I let you go. So let me put you in a dungeon. She does not want you in her land.

GERDA: The Snow Queen does not want me in her land?

KING: No—that's what the Chancellor says. What can I do? Come, Gerda, do let me cast you into the dungeon. A nice dungeon, a comfy one.

GERDA (*deep in thought*): She does not want me in her land . . .

KING (*angry*): How often must I tell you; NO! Come on! If we anger her we are all lost. But if you go to the dungeon the Chancellor promised me that she would turn all my enemies into ice.

(CHANCELLOR *enters at the back and listens.*)

GERDA: If she does not want me in her land, that can only mean that Kay is really there.

CHANCELLOR: It means nothing of the sort!

(GERDA *jumps up. The* KING *rises.*)

34

But may I remind your Majesty of what it may mean if that girl is allowed to get away? Seize her!

KING: But you see, my dear Chancellor, she is on the wrong side of the line.

CHANCELLOR: To that, one might be inclined to say: Fiddlesticks! (*He slowly approaches the line.*) A King must be (a) as cold as snow, (b) as hard as ice and (c) as swift as a—winter whirlwind! (*Suddenly lassoes* GERDA *with his scarf and draws her across the 'frontier'.*)

GERDA: Help! Help! . . .

CHANCELLOR: Haha! That is the way to do it!
(*The* STORYTELLER *suddenly enters on* KING's *half.*)

STORYTELLER (*freeing* GERDA): No, *that's* the way to do it! (*And he runs with her to safety across the line.*)

CHANCELLOR: You—here?

STORYTELLER: Yes, I'm here. (*Embracing* GERDA.) I saw you were following Gerda, so I followed you. Snip Snap! Now what can you do?

CHANCELLOR: Sire, call the guards!

STORYTELLER (*pulling out pistol to* KING): Who moves—is shot! (*Drawing a sword, to* CHANCELLOR.) Who stirs—is stabbed!

CHANCELLOR: Call the guards! He won't shoot. He probably forgot to load it.

STORYTELLER: No, I didn't. (*Engaging the* CHANCELLOR.) Haha! Sir Chancellor!

GERDA: Klaus! Christina!

CHANCELLOR (*fencing*): The guards, sire! The pistol isn't loaded.

KING (*trembling*): He says it is.

CHANCELLOR: If it is—he'll miss.

KING: And if he doesn't? . . . It's I—I who'll be killed!

35

CHANCELLOR: Ridiculous! (*He knocks the pistol out of the* STORYTELLER's *hand with his sword.*) That's that!
(*The* KING *approaches as the* STORYTELLER, *in the heat of battle, puts his foot across the line.*)

GERDA: Look out! The line!
(*The* KING *trips up the* STORYTELLER.)

KING (*proudly*): That's that.

STORYTELLER (*falling*): You tripped me up, Your Majesty! You cheated!

KING (*seizing the* STORYTELLER *by his arms*): Guards! Guards!

GERDA (*seizing the* STORYTELLER *by his legs*): Christina! Klaus!
(*As* KING *and* GERDA *start trying to pull the* STORYTELLER *into their respective halves,* TWO GUARDS *run in on one side and the* PRINCESS *and* PRINCE *on the other. A tug-of-war ensues. At last the* STORYTELLER *is pulled into* CHRISTINA's *half of the room.*)

PRINCE: What's this?

GERDA: They nearly killed my best friend. And they want to cast me into a dungeon.

PRINCE: Let them try.

PRINCESS (*threatening*): Papa, for this I shall . . .

PRINCE (*to* CHRISTINA): Don't waste time on him! (*To* GERDA.) We've brought three fur coats.

PRINCESS: Oh, yes! Let's see which one suits you best.
(CHANCELLOR *and* KING *whisper together.*)

PRINCE: Don't waste time! (*To* GERDA.) Take the first you can get on! . . . (*Loudly.*) What are they whispering about there?

PRINCESS: Papa, if you don't stop plotting . . .

KING: We aren't plotting . . . just chatting . . . of this and that . . .

(*The* RAVENS *enter.*)

KARL AND KLARA: Trara! Trara!

KARL: A *carr*iage is *ready*!

KLARA: Bl*ack* m*ares are har*nessed!

PRINCE: Splendid! Thanks for your services!

(*The* RAVENS *bow.*)

PRINCE: Ready, Gerda?—Christina? (*To* STORYTELLER.) Are you coming with us?

STORYTELLER: No. I'll keep my eye on the Chancellor— to prevent him from following you.

CHANCELLOR: Oh fiddlesticks!

PRINCESS: And Papa, I warn you, if . . .

PRINCE (*impatiently*): Oh come on, Christina!

(*The* PRINCE *and* PRINCESS *go off.*)

KARL AND KLARA (*off*): Tra-ra tra-ra tra-ra tra-ra!

STORYTELLER (*standing aside, keeping his eye on* CHANCELLOR, *but tempted by the triumph of the moment to a little dance*): Snip! Snap! Snooper! Pooper! Bazalooper! . . .

CHANCELLOR (*aside to* KING): Sound the alarm!

KING (*aside to* GUARD): Sound the alarm!

STORYTELLER (*stopping short in dance*): Crippety!

(*Sound of alarm off.*)

Crappity!

(*Alarm.*)

CHANCELLOR: Hahaha! My dear Mr. Storyteller, the game is up. This little story will end soon—and not happily!

STORYTELLER (*not at all sure, but quietly*): Perhaps, my dear Chancellor—— Perhaps not!

(*Alarm.*)

37

CHANCELLOR: The King's guard will catch Gerda and we will throw her into a dungeon. Hahaha! What do you say to that?

STORYTELLER: Perhaps!—just—perhaps!

CHANCELLOR: Why, they cannot fail to catch her now!

STORYTELLER: Perhaps!

(*The* KING *has been looking out excitedly.*)

KING: They've caught her!

STORYTELLER (*perturbed*): What?

KING: My good soldiers caught her! Here they come now! Bring her in!

(*A* GUARD *brings in someone who seems to be* GERDA. *She is crying and covering her face with a muff.*)

STORYTELLER: Gerda! Crippety!

KING: Gerda.

CHANCELLOR: That's that!

KING: That's that! To the dungeons with her!

(*Noise at door.*)

CHANCELLOR: What's that?

KING: Come in!

(*A second* GUARD *brings in another* GERDA, *similarly dressed and weeping.*)

STORYTELLER: Crappity!

(*General amazement.*)

KING (*hand to head*): Oh! I knew all this would drive me mad! Two Gerdas! I've gone off my head!

(*Both 'Gerdas' lower muffs. They are* KLAUS *and* CHRISTINA.)

CHANCELLOR AND KING: WHAT!!!

STORYTELLER: Yes, dear Chancellor—that is that!

KING: But . . . but . . . how is that . . . that? (*Pointing first to* KLAUS, *then to* CHRISTINA.)

PRINCE: Simple! We had three fur coats. Gerda put on one.

PRINCESS: ...And we put on the other two in the dark ...

PRINCE: And the stupid guards ran after us ...

PRINCESS: ...And Gerda simply drove away ...

PRINCE: ...in the golden coach. (*To* CHANCELLOR.) And you can't get her now!

STORYTELLER: Bravo, you two! (*The children run off.*) And now, my dear Chancellor, *is* the game up?

CHANCELLOR: No. The game goes on, my dear Story-teller. (*Exit officiously.*)

STORYTELLER (*to audience*):   But our story—that goes on too! (*Exit mimicking the* CHANCELLOR's *exit.*)

KING (*dejectedly, sitting on throne*):   Oh!
(*Music of coach travelling.*)

CURTAIN

PART TWO

PROLOGUE

House curtain up. Scene curtain still down. Sound of singing off.

STORYTELLER (*singing*): Snip! Snap! Snooper! (*Approaching.*) Pooper, bazalooper!

(*Enter* STORYTELLER, *foot-sore.*)

Snip! Snap! Snooper! Crippety! Crappety!—Ugh!

(*He tries to do his little step dance, but his feet are too sore.*)

Now, look here, feet! I know how many many rocky miles we have walked together. I know you're sore, tired, blistered and needing a bath; but when I say a 'crippety-crappety' to keep my spirits up, don't you go and spoil things by refusing to 'boom' when you come to 'Boom'! What? But if I don't give you some musical stamping to do you'll go cold and freeze among all this snow. What? There! there! Old feet! Don't cry. We'll forgive you this time; for after all we *have* got ahead of Gerda—even with her grand golden coach. Yes, the hilly shortcuts were hard going! We can afford to sit down for a bit. (*He does.*) Ah! The last I saw of Gerda was when we looked back from the top of our shortcut hill; and all the horses' harness in the sun shone like quicksilver; and all their bells rang and echoed up the valley. It may not be very long before her coach jingles by, on the road down there below the wood. On towards Kay in the far, far North!

(*A robber's whistle.*)

Sh! Sh! (*Listens.*)

(*A whistle.*)

41

Oh! Robbers! The robbers' call!
> (*A whistle.*)

Oh! From my right!
> (*A whistle.*)

Oh! From my left!
> (*A whistle.*)

Oh! From my back! I'm surrounded! Crippity. (*Looking about.*) Crappity!

> (*He suddenly sees something in the distance.*)

The golden coach is coming too! Away down the road I can see a little cloud of snow, and now the sun shining on something gold. Oh!

> (*Whistle.*)

The robbers will capture Gerda! I've got to get them away from this road till the coach gets past.

> (*A whistle.*)

Here's a fix! What shall I do! Oh! I've got it! My beard! And my false nose too! (*He gets them out.*) I'll make myself look fierce and then I'll pretend I'm a robber too. A robber won't kill another robber. At least I hope not! I must lead them a dance! (*Making up.*)

> (*Whistle nearer.*)

My nose! My beard! My sword! My gun! Now! (*He stands ready.*)

> (*Enter* TWO ROBBERS, *one from either side.*)

1ST ROBBER: Stand still as a snowman or I'll slit you in two!

2ND ROBBER: Move and you'll never move again!

STORYTELLER (*trying to be brave*): Ha! ha! ha! (*Putting on gruff voice.*) Would you kill off Karel the Cruel? Would you rob the world of a great robber?

1ST ROBBER: Are you Karel the Cruel?

STORYTELLER (*threateningly*):   Must I show you, eh!

1ST ROBBER: No, but . . .

STORYTELLER: Take me to your chief. Quickly!

2ND ROBBER: Maybe we . . .

STORYTELLER (*roaring*):   I said take me to your chief!

2ND ROBBER: Yes sir—I mean—yes.

STORYTELLER (*roaring*):   Take me from here!

1ST ROBBER: Yes, sir; but I'm afraid that we will have to blindfold you to take you to our secret headquarters.

STORYTELLER (*at top of his voice*):   Then blindfold me! (*Aside.*) I hope they don't knock off my nose. I can't hear the golden coach yet.

2ND ROBBER: Here, sir. (*He is blindfolded.*)

STORYTELLER: Now lead on! (*Roaring.*) I said quickly!

BOTH ROBBERS: Yes, sir.

Exeunt TWO ROBBERS *and* STORYTELLER.
Music—sound of travelling coach approaching then fade.

BLACKOUT

SCENE 1

THE ROBBERS' TENT

Before the Curtain goes up, there is the sound of singing and banging.

THE ROBBERS: We live in the woods! We live in the wilds
              A wicked life and a bold!
              With trap and knife and gun and sling
              We hunt for the bear . . . for anything,
              For coins of silver and gold!
CHORUS: For coins of silver and gold!

A ROBBER: Silent the ambush, the trap and the knife—
              But noisy the gun at the rout!
              We like the noise of yells and shots,
              Of soup that's bubbling in the pots,
              We eat and shoot and shout!
CHORUS: We eat and shoot and shout!
                   (Whistle off.)
A ROBBER: We revelling robbers live in the woods
              A wicked but wonderful life!
                (The singer stops.)
ROBBER WOMAN: Look out!
   (They all scramble for their guns and stand ready. The
     STORYTELLER *is led in, blindfolded.)*
   Who is it?
1ST ROBBER: He says he's Karel the Cruel. And he wants
   to join our robber band.

44

ROBBER WOMAN: Never heard of him! Is he fierce enough?

STORYTELLER (*roaring*): Take off this rag, you country cut-purse! Or I'll blow myself up and shatter the camp!

ROBBER WOMAN: Sounds all right! Let's see his face! (*They whip off the handkerchief and almost the beard too.*)

STORYTELLER (*roaring at her*): Woman! Let me see your good chief!

ROBBER WOMAN: You're talking to the chief.

STORYTELLER (*taken aback*): Oh!

ROBBER WOMAN: And don't roar at me . . . or . . . (*Threatening.*)

STORYTELLER: Ahhahahaha! (*Slapping her on the back and laughing.*) I roared at *you*! The chief! Ahahaha! (*She laughs too. They all laugh.*)

ROBBER WOMAN: So you want to join us? What can you do?

STORYTELLER (*flourishing pistol*): I can shoot a man dead at a hundred yards and (*flourishing sword*) . . . at one yard I can hack him into a hundred neat pieces!
(*All laugh.*)

ROBBER WOMAN: Haha! I like you. You're a real robber!

STORYTELLER: I'm glad you think so!
(*Whistle.*)

ROBBER WOMAN: Look out!
(*Enter CHANCELLOR with ROBBERS, also blindfolded.*)

STORYTELLER: Crippety! Crappity! I know these boots!

ROBBER WOMAN: And who is this?

1ST ROBBER: He says . . .

CHANCELLOR (*tearing off handkerchief*): I must see the chief! There's no time to lose.

ROBBER WOMAN: Hm! . . . You are addressing the chief. I took over the business when my husband died. What do you want?

CHANCELLOR: I must talk to you immediately—but in secret.

ROBBER WOMAN: Hm! . . .

STORYTELLER: Chief, don't trust that man!

ROBBER WOMAN: Don't teach me my trade! Hm . . . (*Movement of head to tent.*) In there. (*Let's the* CHANCELLOR *pass in front of her and follows—revolver pointed at him. Turning round in the entrance.*) And no eavesdropping! Or I'll shoot you!

OLOF: Aye, aye, ma'am.

BARBRO: What do you take us for, ma'am?

ROBBER WOMAN (*in the tent*):   If you are going to waste my time over some footling bit of business, you won't leave this place alive.

CHANCELLOR: Fiddlesticks! We shall come to an understanding. But it must be quickly.

ROBBER WOMAN: Hm! (*Slowly.*) Well . . . get on with it!

CHANCELLOR: I can help you to enormous booty.

ROBBER WOMAN: Hm . . . what sort?

CHANCELLOR: A golden coach. It is approaching now. Drawn by four black horses from the royal stables.

ROBBER WOMAN: Hm . . . Who's in the coach?

CHANCELLOR: A little girl.

ROBBER WOMAN: Any guard?

CHANCELLOR: No.

ROBBER WOMAN: Hm. I see . . . How much of the booty . would you want?

CHANCELLOR: Not much.

ROBBER WOMAN: *How* much?

CHANCELLOR: Only the girl.

ROBBER WOMAN: The girl? Why? Who is she?

CHANCELLOR: Oh, just a little girl, a poor girl; you wouldn't get any ransom for her, anyway.

ROBBER WOMAN: Hm! . . . And how does a beggar girl come to be riding in a golden coach? Eh?

CHANCELLOR: It was lent her—by the Prince. A Queen wants her to be stopped.

ROBBER WOMAN: Hm! . . .

CHANCELLOR: Be quick. I only want the girl and I'll take her away in my coach and not bother you.

ROBBER WOMAN: Is this golden coach near?

CHANCELLOR: O very near. We *must* hurry!

ROBBER WOMAN: Hm! . . . (*Whistles.*)

(BARBRO *pops head in.*)

Telescope! (*He goes.*) If the coach is anywhere near, it will be on the road.

(BARBRO *hands in telescope.*)

(*To* BARBRO.) Watch this one! (*Nodding to* CHANCELLOR.)

BARBRO (*drawing long knife*): Aye! Aye! Chief!

(ROBBER WOMAN *puts telescope through hole in tent and looks.*)

ROBBER WOMAN: Hm! . . . It's there all right! Coming bowling along in the snow, glittering in the sun like . . .

CHANCELLOR: . . . Gold.

ROBBER WOMAN: Yes . . . gold.

BARBRO: Gold!

ROBBER WOMAN: Sound the horn!

BARBRO: Aye, aye!

(*He fetches horn off hook and blows. An answering horn signal from outside; the sound of a drum; calls; a clatter of arms.*)

ROBBER WOMAN (*girding herself with sword*):   Barbro! Send somebody to guard this man.

(BARBRO *exits. She turns to the* CHANCELLOR; *very quietly.*) Well, if you have tricked me, and my men fall into an ambush, you will not leave this place alive.

CHANCELLOR: Fiddlesticks! Better hurry up! Or you'll miss the coach!

ROBBER WOMAN (*threateningly*):   Would you teach me my trade? Hm?

(*The bearded* STORYTELLER *sticks his head into the tent.*)

STORYTELLER (*roaring*):   You want me, chief?

ROBBER WOMAN: Yes. Come in. (*He enters.*) You are not coming with us.

STORYTELLER: Not?—Chief, take me with you! I'm a tiger in battle! Grrrr! (*Another roar, thumping chest.*)

ROBBER WOMAN: There won't be a battle. There's only a coachman and a girl.

STORYTELLER: A girl? Take me, chief! I'll kill her!

ROBBER WOMAN: What for?

STORYTELLER: I've hated children since I was . . . so high.

ROBBER WOMAN: You stay here and look after this man. Don't answer or—— (*Pointing her pistol at him.*)

STORYTELLER (*quickly*):   Right you are, Mrs. Chief!

ROBBER WOMAN (*going off*):   I am always right.

STORYTELLER: Quite right, Mrs. Chief.

CHANCELLOR (*very satisfied, humming to himself*):   Twice two is four!—Everything goes well.—Twice two is four.— Everything is going as it should. . . .

(*From far away the voice of the* ROBBER WOMAN *is heard:* To horse! *and the clatter of hoofs, and shouting.*)

(*To the* STORYTELLER.) So you, too, hate children, Robber?

48

STORYTELLER: Children?—Vermin! Should be stamped out!

CHANCELLOR: My very opinion!
   (*Shouts and cries are again heard in the distance.*)
   Aha! (*He takes the telescope.*) Let's see what's going on down the road. (*Putting the telescope through the hole in the tent.*)

STORYTELLER (*very excited*):   Can you see something?

CHANCELLOR (*looking through the telescope*): Ha! ha! Very amusing!

STORYTELLER (*anxiously*):   What is?

CHANCELLOR: The coachman is whipping up the horses like mad.

STORYTELLER: And?

CHANCELLOR: Gold is rather heavy. Ha! ha! The coach won't go fast enough.

STORYTELLER: And our men?

CHANCELLOR: The robbers? Ah! There they go sweeping along! The front horse is down in a cloud of snow! The coach is stopped! They're all round it now. The coachman is jumping from the box and running away. They've got him! Someone's leapt on the coach.
   (*Shouts off in the distance.*)
   Ha! ha! Good-night now, my little Gerda! (*He turns from the telescope.*) Twice two is four. That's that!

STORYTELLER: I hope they didn't kill G— the little girl?

CHANCELLOR (*suspiciously*):   Why? What's that to you?

STORYTELLER (*hurriedly*):   Because I'd like to kill her myself. Ha!

CHANCELLOR: Ha! ha! Robber, I like you. Here they come!
   (*Noise. Joyful shouts. The* ROBBER WOMAN *and the gang of*

49   E

ROBBERS, *with* GERDA *in their midst, appear, dancing with excitement.* BARBRO *sings* 'A wicked and wonderful life'.)

ROBBER WOMAN (*to* CHANCELLOR): Hey you, stranger, you are free! You didn't cheat us.

CHANCELLOR: Yes, but may I remind you . . . our agreement? The girl?

ROBBER WOMAN: You can take her.

GERDA (*freeing herself*): No—no!

CHANCELLOR: Quiet!

GERDA (*While* ROBBERS *catch her again and push her towards the* CHANCELLOR): Wait, robbers, wait, please, just one little minute!

CHANCELLOR: Silence, I say!

GERDA: Take my fur coat, my fur hat, my gloves, my muff—take what you like—but let me go, dear robbers!

BARBRO (*laughing*): 'Dear Robbers.'

ROBBERS: Hahaha!

GERDA: Have I said anything funny?

CHANCELLOR: Bring her here!

(*At this moment a girl,* WENKI, *bursts into the tent, small, full of life, a rifle hanging over her shoulder and a pistol in her girdle. With a whoop she jumps on her mother's back.*)

ROBBER WOMAN: Hi!

WENKI: Hullo, old Mother!

ROBBER WOMAN: Hullo, you young goat!

WENKI: Hullo, you old goat! (*Slapping each other.*)

ROBBER WOMAN: Haha! How was the hunt, daughter?

WENKI: Good. A hare and a wild goose. And your hunt?

ROBBER WOMAN: Not so bad! A golden coach, four black horses *and* a young girl!

WENKI: A girl! (*Shouting.*) Where? (*Seeing* GERDA.) Ah! Old goat, I'll have the girl.

CHANCELLOR: But you can't! She's mine.

WENKI: Who's the old codger with the frozen face?

CHANCELLOR: You can't . . .

WENKI: Don't you dare say 'no' to me! Bah! (*Taking* GERDA *to corner.*) Come, little girl. And don't tremble! I hate people who are scared and when I hate people I . . .

GERDA: . . . No, really. I'm not scared. (*Terrified.*) Just excited, and happy.

WENKI (*patting* GERDA):   You little pet! You must play with me and go hunting.

CHANCELLOR: I protest, I protest.

WENKI: Shoot the old fool! (*Turning to* GERDA.) Don't be afraid. Nobody shall shoot you as long as I don't quarrel with you. And even then I'll shoot you myself— I like you so much. (*The two girls whisper together.*)

CHANCELLOR (*to* ROBBER WOMAN):   But, madam, I protest! I protest!

ROBBER WOMAN (*indifferent*):   My daughter wants the girl to herself. I never refuse her anything. Now get along!

CHANCELLOR: I protest!

ROBBER WOMAN: Alright, but protest somewhere else. Get out!

(*Sound of coach drawn into camp.*)

Ah, that is the golden coach. Let's break it up and share the bits out! Come on!

ROBBERS (*running out*):   Booty! The coach! Gold!

(GERDA, WENKI, *the* CHANCELLOR *and the* STORYTELLER *remain.* GERDA *and* WENKI *have talked together for some time.*)

WENKI: So, you're called Gerda. Nice name. I . . .
(*The* CHANCELLOR *breathes on* WENKI.)

What the . . . ! (*Turning to see* CHANCELLOR.) You still here? (*Pointing pistol.*) Get out!

        (CHANCELLOR *breathes again.*)

(*Mimics him, breathing three times.*) I'll count three. If at 'three' you're still here, then . . . (*Aims at* CHANCELLOR.) . . . One . . .

CHANCELLOR: I . . .

WENKI: Two . . .

CHANCELLOR: I . . .

WENKI: Thrrrr . . .

    (*The* CHANCELLOR *runs out.* WENKI *and* GERDA *laugh, and even the* STORYTELLER *can't keep his face straight.*)

(*To the* BEARDED MAN.) What are you doing here?

STORYTELLER: Allow me, little chief, just to say a word to our new friend . . .

WENKI: No! Get out!

STORYTELLER: But . . .

WENKI (*levelling her pistol at him*):   One . . .

STORYTELLER: Listen . . .

WENKI: Two . . .

STORYTELLER: But . . .

WENKI: Thrrrr . . .

        (STORYTELLER *runs out quickly.*)

(*Laughing.*) Haha! That's settled. Oh, Gerda, how nice you look! Your coat! And what gloves! You must give them to me. And your fur boots and muff. Friends must share everything. You don't mind, do you?

GERDA: No . . . not at all . . . only . . . without the things . . . I'll probably die of cold before I get to the Snow Queen.

WENKI: The Snow Queen?

GERDA: Yes, that's where I am going.

WENKI: Nonsense! I shan't let you. We have just made friends and now I'll keep you here. You'll like it, Gerda! I have a whole zoo here, you know: a reindeer, pigeons, dogs and guinea-pigs! But I like you better, Gerda, my new little pet! Do you want to see my reindeer? (*Runs to a flap in the tent.*) He's here. (*She opens the flap, calling.*) Come here! (*Whistles.*) It can speak!

> (*The head of a* REINDEER *appears in the flap.*)

GERDA: It can speak?

WENKI: Yes! Beautifully! It is a rare type from the far north.

GERDA (*hesitating*): The far north? . . . Oh—may I ask him something?

WENKI: Yes. Go on! Make him talk.

GERDA: Reindeer . . . do you know . . . where the land of the Snow Queen lies? . . .

> (REINDEER *nods his head.*)

WENKI (*furious*): What's that? Hoi! Away with you! (*She shuts the flap.*) I shan't let you go there, Gerda—no—no —no! (*Goes to tent entrance and calls.*) Heh! You! You with the beard!

STORYTELLER (*appearing before the tent*): What is it, little chief?

WENKI: Get a bed ready for my friend here!

STORYTELLER: Aye, aye, little chief.

WENKI (*searching for a rope*): And see that it's warm and soft! Straw and skins! and hurry up!

> (*The* STORYTELLER *mumbles something and busies himself near* GERDA.)

GERDA (*shrieks*): Ai!

WENKI: What's up?

GERDA: He pulled my dress.

WENKI (*to* STORYTELLER):   How dare you?

STORYTELLER: I only shook a beetle off her dress.

WENKI: Beetle!—I'll beetle you! Is the bed ready? Yes?
Then get out! (*She aims her pistol at him.*) One . . .
(*The* STORYTELLER *runs off.*)
(*Laughing.*) How he runs!—But Gerda, now let's talk
seriously: once and for all, I won't allow you to go. You
must stay with me, and I shall tie you up with a triple
secret robber knot to this tent-peg. (*While doing it.*) And
don't cry or I shall shoot you, for I can't stand tears!
(*Kneels down and with kindness whispers to her.*) You see, I
would let you go—but just imagine—how *could* I part with
you! How could I? Now don't answer back! Be good—
lie down! . . . That's it.—You know, I always fall asleep
at once. I do everything quickly. So must you. And
don't try to undo the rope! Have you a knife?

GERDA: No.

WENKI (*smiling*):   You don't need one either. (*Kisses her.*)
Sleep well. (*Rises and goes to the exit where she turns round
once again whispering.*) Good-night, my own little pet pig!
(*She goes off.*)

GERDA: Good-night!
(*Silence. It is now rather dark outside the tent and inside there
burns only a small oil-lamp.* GERDA *turns on her bed—
sighs.*)
Oh! . . . (*Softly.*) Kay! . . . Kay! . . .
(*A shadow appears outside the tent. Somebody enters and creeps
to* GERDA; *it is the* STORYTELLER.)
(*Jumping up.*) Who is it?

STORYTELLER: Hush! I have come to save you! (*Swinging
his knife.*)

GERDA: Oh!

STORYTELLER: Hush! (*He cuts the rope.*)

GERDA: Who . . . who . . . are . . . you?

(*The* STORYTELLER *takes off his beard and false nose.*)

STORYTELLER: Gerda!

GERDA: You? Mr. Storyteller! (*In his arms.*) How did you come here?

STORYTELLER: I disguised myself as one of the robbers to try to keep them away from your coach.

GERDA: But where did you get the beard and the nose?

STORYTELLER: I've had them with me since I first followed the Chancellor. I always carry my nose in my pocket! Many noses! (*He shows them to* GERDA.) But now, let's run! We can get some horses in the next village . . .

(GERDA *and* STORYTELLER *hurriedly search the tent for* GERDA's *belongings. But there are noises outside: human voices, laughter . . .*)

What's that?

GERDA: The robbers coming back.

(*Steps outside.*)

STORYTELLER: Lie down!

(ROBBER WOMAN *and* ROBBERS *enter.*)

ROBBER WOMAN: What's that?

STORYTELLER (*forgetting to put on his beard, but acting the bad robber, turning to* GERDA *and roaring ferociously*):   Girrr!! If you move, I'll kill you! I've killed as many people as I have hairs in this long beard of mine!

ROBBER WOMAN: Who's that?

STORYTELLER: That? It's the little girl, she was trying . . .

ROBBER WOMAN (*interrupting and pointing at* STORYTELLER): No—that! Who's that?

STORYTELLER: What a question! That's me. Don't you recognise me, chief?

ROBBER WOMAN (*drily*): No.

STORYTELLER (*aside*): Crippety!—where is my beard? (*Aloud.*) I . . . I . . . I've shaved, chief.

BARBRO: Yes!—and you've shaved your nose off too!
(*The* STORYTELLER *involuntarily claps his hand to his nose. Excitement of the* ROBBERS.)

ROBBER WOMAN: Grab him!

ROBBERS (*throwing themselves upon the* STORYTELLER): Traitor! Spy! Blood-hound!

GERDA: Help! Help!
(WENKI *runs in with her pistol in hand.*)

WENKI: What's up? Who's dared to touch you? Who . . . Who's that?

GERDA: My friend, the Storyteller. Don't kill him, please! He knows such beautiful stories, lots of them! And he came only to save me.

WENKI: Save you? You wanted to run away? . . .
(*A moment of silence.*)

GERDA: I would have left you a letter.
(*The* ROBBERS *laugh.*)

WENKI (*almost crying with rage*): Clear out! All of you! (*Throws herself on the* ROBBERS.) And you, Mother, go! All—go! Go and divide your booty! Get out!
(*The* ROBBERS *laugh and exeunt with* ROBBER WOMAN, *driven off by* WENKI. GERDA *takes* STORYTELLER *by the hand and sits down with him in a corner of the tent.*)

(*To them, looking down at* GERDA, *more calmly.*) Oh, Gerda, Gerda, aren't you ashamed of yourself?

GERDA: No, dear Wenki, no—forgive me. You see, I must try to find my friend, Kay . . .

WENKI: Kay?

STORYTELLER (*confidentially*):   Yes, he was kidnapped by the Snow Queen . . .

GERDA (*looking up*):   Wenki! Please, do let me go. (*No reply.*) Then let me at least talk to the Reindeer. He may have seen Kay. Do let me ask him another question.

STORYTELLER: Do let her!

GERDA: Please!

WENKI (*suddenly, after a short silence*):   Alright. But just one question. (*She opens the flap.*) Reindeer! Come here!

(*The* REINDEER'S *head appears in the flap.*)

GERDA (*getting up*):   Please, tell me, Reindeer—have you ever seen the Snow Queen?

(REINDEER *nods his head.*)

He has. . . . And . . . tell me . . . have you . . . ever . . . seen a little boy with her? . . .

(REINDEER *nods his head.*)

GERDA AND WENKI: He has! (*Grasping each other's hands.*)

GERDA: He's seen him, seen him, too!

WENKI: Tell us at once—where, when?

REINDEER: I was running in the snowy fields . . . It was very bright . . . and suddenly . . . I saw . . . the Snow Queen passing . . . I said to her . . . 'Good evening' . . . but she did not answer. . . . She was talking to a boy . . . 'Kay,' she said . . .

GERDA AND WENKI (*looking at each other*):   Kay!

REINDEER: Great white birds drew their sledge. . . . And the boy smiled. . . . He looked white . . . and cold. . . .

GERDA: You see, I knew it! He was white and cold! Wenki! Please, let me go, Wenki!

REINDEER: Let her go. . . .

WENKI: No, no. (*She wants to shut the flap.*)

57

REINDEER: Let her go, let her go. . . . She can ride on my back . . . to the Snow Queen's land. . . . There is my birthplace, too . . . and many reindeers run there quite free—over the white snow-fields.

WENKI (*after a silence, turning to* GERDA):   And you want to go?

GERDA (*nods*):   Yes. I must.
     (*A long silence.* WENKI *looks at* GERDA. *Then she starts patting the* REINDEER.)

WENKI: He used to amuse me so much. . . . (*Pulling herself together.*) Never mind. Here, take your fur coat, your fur cap and fur gloves. . . . No—I'll keep them; I like them so much. Take Mother's mittens instead. Here! You mustn't look so sad, you must look happy. But now, go! At once! Quickly! No, stop. Take my musical box. This musical box used to make me dance when I was too angry to speak. Then I was happy. Play it if you feel lonely on the white snow-fields. Now——

GERDA (*kissing her*):   Thank you.

REINDEER (*withdrawing his head*):   Thank you. . . .

STORYTELLER (*approaching*):   Thank you.

WENKI (*to the* STORYTELLER):   You needn't thank me. You are going to stay and amuse me with stories till . . . Gerda . . . comes back.

STORYTELLER: But I . . .

WENKI: It's settled. (*Quickly.*) And now go, Gerda!

GERDA (*hesitating*):   Good-bye. I . . .

WENKI (*insistent*):   Go! Go! Before I change my mind! Quick! Go!
     (GERDA *disappears into the night. A silence during which we hear reindeer hoofs on snow.*)
(*To* STORYTELLER.) Why do you stand there gaping? Say

something! Tell me a story, a funny story! If you don't
make me laugh, I will . . . (*Pointing pistol*) One . . .

STORYTELLER (*hurriedly*): Once upon a time, many years
ago, there lived a snowman. He stood in the yard, in
front of the kitchen window. And every time the kitchen
stove spat fire the snowman trembled with fear. (*Slowing
down.*) And one day he said . . . Poor girl . . . quite
alone now when the ice cracks and groans and the terrible winds whistle. And in the midst of the icebergs
lives the Snow Queen, who is so cruel . . . Oh . . .
Gerda . . . She will be so lonely there . . .

WENKI (*rubbing the tears off her eyes*): You were telling me
. . . a story . . . what did . . . Gerda . . . the Snow Queen
. . . the snowman . . . do go on . . . or I shall shoot . . .
(*Crying.*) One . . . two . . . (*She sobs.*)

CURTAIN

SCENE 2

ON THE ROAD TO THE NORTH

Weird 'bird music'. Light slowly comes up on GERDA, *who stands near* REINDEER. *They are looking out into the distance.*

GERDA: How cold it is out here!

(REINDEER *nods.*)

And how quiet, with nothing living . . . not even a tree.

REINDEER (*almost whispering*):   No one goes further north than this.

GERDA: But we must go on. We must find Kay.

REINDEER: We are in the Snow Queen's land now. It is dangerous here.

GERDA: If you are afraid you may stay. I must go on.

REINDEER: But you can see for yourself there is nothing there. . . .

GERDA: Somewhere out there is Kay. The Ice Palace of the Snow Queen *must* be somewhere.

REINDEER: But it is miles and miles and miles away.

GERDA: In which direction?

REINDEER: Straight to the north, where you see the cold light flickering in the sky.

GERDA: Then I must go.

REINDEER: Please, Gerda! No one who has gone to the Ice Palace has ever come back.

GERDA: How will I recognise it? (*Pause.*) You must tell me.

REINDEER (*Sadly.*)   Oh! (*realising she is determined*):

As you near the entrance you will come in sight of the Ice Birds and Bears. The Palace is white.

Huge snowdrifts are its outer walls;
and inside are a thousand halls,
with mirrors of ice, where the Queen may see
herself glide by, silently,
from a thousand angles.
        The windows and doors
are frozen winds and all the floors
are ice a thousand metres deep;
and the ceilings black clouds where the Queen keeps
all the world's snow.
        (Silence.)
(Continuing.) If Kay is in there—he may be dead.

GERDA: No! I must hurry.

REINDEER: If you must go, dear Gerda, go quickly now;
for at this time the Snow Queen may be away, flying her
black cloud to the warm south to sprinkle the moun-
tains with snow.
        (Sigh of wind.)
(Turning.) I cannot go with you. But I will wait by the
red berry tree which stands just outside the Snow Queen's
land. I shall wait for you till I die.
        (Wind.)
(Fearfully.) Oh! Good-bye, Gerda! (REINDEER *runs away*.)
Good-bye!

GERDA *(still looking north)*:   Good-bye, Reindeer! *(Pause.)*
I must not be afraid. Dear God, help me! Oh! Where
the snow meets the sky I think I see something glittering.
It must be . . . the Ice Palace. I am coming, Kay!

*Slowly and fearfully she begins to move to the north: the wind
sighs and light fades on weird 'bird music'.*

BLACKOUT

SCENE 3

IN THE SNOW QUEEN'S PALACE

As the light comes up slowly, we hear the 'bird music'. Then silence.

KAY is revealed seated on the ice throne of the SNOW QUEEN. He is rigid except for his lips, which are moving.

KAY (*slowly in a cold monotone*): Three million million thousands and one, and two, and three, four, five, six, seven, eight, nine . . .

(*Suddenly the weird music announcing the approach of the SNOW QUEEN sounds again. She enters.*)

SNOW QUEEN (*smiling*): Are you still thinking about your figures?

KAY: Yes.

SNOW QUEEN: Think about them while I am gone, Kay.

KAY: Gone?

SNOW QUEEN: Yes, I must leave you all alone in my palace. But only for a very short time. I shall fly on my black cloud far, far away to the warm south, to sprinkle the mountain-tops with snow.

KAY: Three thousand miles to the south.

SNOW QUEEN: How clever you are. With your brain and your heart of ice. . . . (*Suddenly with anxiety.*) Do you feel cold?

KAY: No.

SNOW QUEEN: Really not?

KAY: No.

SNOW QUEEN: I must kiss you again so that your heart does not melt while I am away.

(She kisses him and he freezes still more.)
You are mine, for ever and always!

KAY *(dully)*: Always.

SNOW QUEEN *(to herself)*: No one shall take you from me ... My polar bears and my ice birds guard the door —and even if any creatures passed them, they would never find their way to you, through all the thousand empty icy halls of my palace. ... *(Then aloud again.)* Now, polar wind, come and cut through these icy walls ... and carry me away—to the south!

(She begins to dance, generating the speed of the north wind— then she sweeps through the walls. The music ends abruptly and there is silence. KAY sits motionless and thinks and thinks. Suddenly GERDA'S voice is heard far away and echoing through the palace.)

GERDA *(off and distant)*: Ka-ay! Ka-ay!

     (KAY does not seem to hear.)

(Nearer.) Ka-ay!   Ka-ay!

     (KAY still does not move.)

(Still nearer.) Ka-ay!

     (GERDA comes in.)

(Murmuring, as she crosses and searches without seeing the immobile KAY.) How cold it is. I won't get frozen! I won't get frozen!

     (She turns, about to go, when she sees KAY.)

Kay!

(GERDA runs to him and is about to climb up the steps and throw her arms around him when she stops aghast.)

(In a hushed voice.) Kay ... What is it? You are not ... all frozen ... to death? Kay! Speak to me! Kay, say something! Say my name. Say ... 'Gerda'.

KAY *(in dead tones)*: 'Gerda.'

GERDA: You *can* speak! Oh, Kay, it is really you! You are so changed. Say it's really you, say 'Gerda, I am real'.

KAY (*in same tone*):   'Gerda, I am real.' Go.

GERDA: Kay, how can you speak to me like that? If you only knew how I have walked and walked and searched and gone through haunted castles and robbers' camps and past enormous polar bears . . .

KAY: Go! I am thinking.

GERDA: What are you thinking?

KAY: Figures—until the Snow Queen comes back.

GERDA (*terrified*):   The Snow Queen!—Kay, do come with me, out of this icy place. . . . Don't you remember how good life was at home? Kay—have you forgotten everything?

KAY: I forget nothing.

GERDA: Then you must remember . . . how we played together, hide and seek . . . and . . . and how we used to bathe in the river on a sunny day; and we'd lie and dry on the warm meadow; and how you laughed when I got frightened of the ants and caterpillars when they crept over my neck.

KAY: Go, you make me feel cold.

GERDA: Since you've been away I can swim now; but with one foot on the bottom.

KAY: I feel cold. Leave me! I must think!

GERDA (*quickly following up advantage*):   Kay, remember home and our garret, with the stove you used to light, and the rose-tree . . .

KAY: The rose-tree?

GERDA: And Granny, and Mr. Storyteller!

KAY (*falsely*):   No! I remember nothing! I don't know you! (*In panic.*) Two million million . . .

GERDA: Kay—don't you remember how we looked down into the street, and . . . and the song of our old organ-grinder? (*She sings.*)

> Now the frost grips all the earth,
> The birds begin to cry
> Tears which fall
> And freeze till all
> As snow-flakes fill the sky.
>
> So all the snow-flakes
> Are tears that are silently
> Gliding by . . .
>
> For unless
> God's sun will bless
> Our Earth, the birds must die . . .

(*Little by little,* KAY *is drawn to the song and finally is humming it with* GERDA—*whose singing turns into weeping. As her tears fall on his hands,* KAY *suddenly moves them to his breast.*)

KAY: I feel so cold. . . . What is happening to us?

GERDA (*looking up at* KAY—*then realising that he is awake*): Kay! (*She throws her arms around his neck.*) Kay, you are Kay again, the old Kay!

KAY: I want to go home! Oh, Gerda! Take me home. You know the way. Gerda, don't cry!

GERDA: I am happy, Kay!

KAY: Gerda! Help me down, Gerda! Take me away before the Snow Queen comes! . . . Oh, I can't walk . . .

GERDA: You must. Try! Lean on me. . . . Try! Try!

KAY: I'm trying.

GERDA: See! . . . You can. . . . That's it! . . . That's it!
See. . . . Now you can walk by yourself. . . . Come! . . .
Come! . . . I know the way to the palace door. If we can
get past the bears out there, the Reindeer will be waiting
for us. He is waiting on the snow-field by the bush with
the red berries. If only we can reach him in time he will
carry us away . . . to the south. Hurry!

KAY (*as he moves painfully out*):   We are going back . . . (*In
a sort of wonder.*) . . . Home . . .

*They go slowly, both humming the song of the organ-grinder.
The lights fade.*

BLACKOUT

SCENE 4

OUTSIDE THE PALACE

The light slowly returns. A kind of huge iceberg appears in an unreal light. A dark hole can be seen leading into the ice. Near this 'door' there are POLAR BEARS *guarding the entrance.* FANTASTIC BIRDS *are sitting on a rock of ice.* GERDA *and* KAY *appear from inside the dark hole in the ice—peeping out at the* BEARS, *with a worried expression.*

GERDA (*in a whisper*):   They are awake. If only you could run we would get past.

> (GERDA *pulls* KAY *through the hole—they quickly run past the* BEARS. GERDA *carries a bundle.* KAY *is looking at the sky.*)

KAY (*amazed*):   Gerda . . . look . . . the sky . . . the sky . . . real sky!

GERDA (*worried*):   Yes, Kay, yes, but come as quickly as you can—and don't speak.

> (*They move slowly forward. The* BEARS *move and look up.*)

Oh! (*Stopping.*) They have seen us, Kay. It's too late . . .

> (*The* BEARS *stare at* GERDA *and* KAY *and get up slowly.*)

KAY: Gerda, bears—real live bears!

GERDA: Oh! Please, dear bears, don't touch us now. It wouldn't be fair, because, you see, Kay can't run.

> (*But the* BEARS *approach—*GERDA *tries to shield* KAY *with her body, retreating slowly, while* KAY *is not really aware of any danger.*)

Oh dear! What can we do now? If only I could please them somehow. (*The* BEARS *still come on.* GERDA *clutches*

her bundle anxiously—she feels the musical box in the bundle.)
Ah! The musical box! The musical box, which Wenki
gave me! (*Searching feverishly.*) Where is it?—where . . .
ah, here. . . . Quick—quick. (*Begins to play the musical
box.*) Dance, dear bears—dance. . . .
(*The* BEARS *stop in their advance and begin to turn slowly.*)

KAY: Music . . . Gerda, music . . . (*Waving his hands to
the time, he looks at his fingers.*) Oh! My fingers can move!
See!

(*The* BIRDS *start moving to the rhythm of* GERDA'S *music, and
sing. The* BEARS *dance.*)

(*Seeing the* BEARS.) The bears are dancing, Gerda! They
are dancing!! They are happy. I am happy. If only I
could dance too.

(KAY *in his joyful excitement begins to beat time, first only
with one hand, then clapping both. Slowly his body begins to
move, he stamps his still half paralysed feet which gradually
move more and more freely. Then he starts jumping until—
a real boy—he falls into a kind of folk-dance, shouting with
joy. He has become the centre of the scene. The* BIRDS *have
stopped their singing, the* BEARS *their dancing, they only
stamp to the rhythm of* KAY'S *dance. They all look at* KAY
and gradually become affected by his outbursts of happiness.
GERDA *laughs, the animals shout—it is a scene of general
merriment.*)

GERDA: Isn't he funny, bears? (*She laughs.*) Oh, Kay,
stop it—stop it. (*She stops playing.*)

(*The* BEARS *growl, the* BIRDS *chatter.*)

We must go quickly, Kay, and you are quite hot, silly
boy, and out of breath. You'll catch cold. (*While she
binds her scarf around his neck.*) Won't he, bears?

(*The* BEARS *nod.*)

KAY (*patting them*):   Oh! I love the bears. I love everyone.
  (*Suddenly the sky is overcast.*)

GERDA (*looking up*):   Oh! A great black cloud is approaching. (*Suddenly.*) Kay! If this is the Snow Queen! We'd
  better run. Come!

KAY: Good-bye, bears!

GERDA: Good-bye, birds!

  (*The wind suddenly grows very loud.*)

KAY (*stops* GERDA, *he listens*):   Gerda! . . . The Snow
  Queen! The Snow Queen is coming!

  (*The wind howls louder.* GERDA *and* KAY *crouch closely
  together, while the* BEARS *stand and shield them. Suddenly
  something appears amidst the falling flakes . . . whirls
  across the stage . . . and disappears through the wall of ice
  into the palace: it is the* SNOW QUEEN. *A long silence.*)
  (*Whispering.*) The Snow Queen!

GERDA (*whispering too*):   If only you could run fast!

KAY!   But I can! See, I can run like the wind! (*Joyfully
  running off.*) I can run! I can run! (*Off.*) Come on, Gerda!

GERDA (*shouting after him and following*):   To the south,
  Kay! To the bush with the red berries!

KAY (*in distance*):   Run! Run!

  (*A new gust of wind . . . and then there is a call in the distance
  —the call of the* SNOW QUEEN.)

SNOW QUEEN (*off stage*):   Kay. . . . (*Then louder.*) Kay? . . .
  (*And finally a scream.*) Kay!

  (*The* SNOW QUEEN *appears in the palace entrance . . . she
  stops there.*)

  (*After a long silence.*) Kay. . . .

The light slowly dies.

BLACKOUT

69

SCENE 5

ON THE WAY BACK

The wind heard in the dark is still howling as the light returns.

The STORYTELLER *enters, followed by* WENKI. *Both are apparently fighting against the wind.*

STORYTELLER (*sighing*):   Gerda. . . . Will we ever find her? Oh, my poor tired feet!

WENKI: Stop moaning!—One more sigh out of you and (*drawing her knife*)—say good-bye to life! (*Turning away.*) (*Great sigh from* STORYTELLER.) You! . . . (*Speechless.*)

STORYTELLER: I can't help it! It's my feet that sigh—not me. They're so tired of me—just like you.

(WENKI *laughs, so does* STORYTELLER *as he sits down.*)

WENKI (*sitting down near him*):   Oh! Can't you *do* something to find her.

STORYTELLER: Perhaps now the winter is over . . .

WENKI: Perhaps! Always 'Perhaps'! We should not have come back to the King's castle. We should have gone on to the North.

STORYTELLER: Perhaps!

WENKI: Oh! Don't sit there and . . .

STORYTELLER (*listening*):   Sh! Sh! Did you hear something? (*We hear the 'Kra-Kra' of a* RAVEN. *The* RAVEN *appears, unnoticed by the two, and stands watching them. It is* KARL, *now wearing a ribbon around his chest.*)

WENKI: No. You're imagining things. You are always

imagining things. (*Looking up.*) Ugh—this spring! It's dreadful.

KARL: A nasty March, yes.

(STORYTELLER *and* WENKI *jump and turn round.*)

STORYTELLER: But . . . it's Karl! Surely it's Karl!

KARL (*nodding and hopping about*): Karl, Karl, for my friends I'm always Karl!—For others I am now an 'Excellency'! (*Proudly arranging the ribbon with his beak.*) 'Excellency Karl', isn't that grand? (*Proudly giggling.*) Ra-ra!

STORYTELLER: His Excellency Karl. May I introduce you to Miss Wenki—a friend of Gerda. (*Bowing grandly.*)

KARL (*bowing*): Glad—glad—glad—to have met you!

WENKI (*with a little curtsey*): How do you do?

STORYTELLER: And how are you all?

KARL: Hah . . . Klata and I are married.

STORYTELLER: Congratulations.

KARL: And travelling with Klaus and Christina.

STORYTELLER: So that's why we didn't find any of you at the castle.

KARL: Yes. Klaus has commanded the whole army to make one massive search party, to find Gerda. Ah! Our Prince has a plan!

STORYTELLER: And what is your part in the plan?

KARL (*with modesty*): I just hover in advance casting glances over the land.

STORYTELLER: And have you found anything?

KARL: Rather!

STORYTELLER AND WENKI (*eagerly*): What?

KARL: I have found you.

WENKI (*disappointed*): Oh! (STORYTELLER *sits again.*) No one's getting anywhere! I can't stand it!

KARL (*tragically*): Yes, in fact—when you mark—that months are passing—and nothing happens—it shatters one's nerves in unbearable fashion. . . . (*Changing mood.*) Hahaha! Don't I talk grandly?

WENKI (*rudely*): Pah!

(KARL *is hurt.*)

STORYTELLER (*amused*): It's alright, Karl. You are wonderful, a true court raven! (*Very formally.*) Would you be good enough to lead us to their Royal Highnesses?

KARL: And Klara, and Klara! They *are* not far!

STORYTELLER: And Klara, of course. Do fly ahead of us, please.

KARL (*sharply*): I do not 'fly'. An 'Excellency' does not 'fly'—he *hovers*.

STORYTELLER: Sorry, please 'hover' ahead!

KARL (*bowing to* WENKI): Ladies first!

WENKI: Thank you . . . sir. (*Goes off.*)

STORYTELLER: After you, Karl.

KARL: *After* you—*after* you!

STORYTELLER (*bowing again*): No really, after you, Mr. Karl.

KARL: *After* you—*after* you!

STORYTELLER: Oh—you are just too kind, your Excellency! (*Exit with yet another bow.*)

KARL (*very pleased*): Haven't we marvellous manners?—Grand!

(*Swelling with pride he follows the others. The stage is empty for a moment. Another gust of wind. Then* KAY *enters quickly, from where* STORYTELLER *and* WENKI *entered before.*)

KAY: Raven! Raven! (*He stops, disappointed.*) There he flies. . . . (*Calling back.*) Here, Gerda! . . . Do hurry up! . . .

(GERDA *enters, very tired.—The wind howls.*)

GERDA: I can't—— (KAY *runs to help her.*)

KAY: Come on, just a bit further. Try! There must be a house somewhere. There was a raven but it flew off before I could ask it the way.

GERDA: A raven? (*Wondering.*) No, it couldn't be. There are thousands of ravens. I am so tired. Since the Reindeer left us . . .

KAY: Ah! What a fine ride that was!

GERDA: Yes—but since then we have been running and hiding so, and hiding and running that now I can't go another step—not even if the Snow Queen is on our tracks. I've never seen so many dark threatening snow clouds in all my life.

KAY: We shall leave them behind. Spring is coming, Gerda! And summer! Think of that and try to struggle on.

GERDA: If we'd only found Wenki at the robbers' camp, or the Prince and Princess at the castle. . . . Where can they all be?

KAY (*after a look at the sky*):   Gerda, I'm afraid that something fresh is brewing!

(*It gets dark—rather quickly.*)

GERDA: Oh! The Snow Queen? Again?

KAY: Come—we'll hide in that thicket! (*He leads her to it.*) Lean on me! Good Gerda!

(*The children hide. The wind now reaches a new pitch of violence. The* CHANCELLOR *appears. He has his eyes glued to the ground. Whenever he comes near the thicket the children duck behind it.*)

CHANCELLOR (*humming*):   Twice two is four, everything is going well . . . twice two is four. Aha! Tracks in the

73

snow! Two feet of the boy—two feet of the girl—twice two is . . . (*Speaking.*) No . . . there are twice four feet . . . twice four is . . . (*He counts the tracks.*) . . . eight! Where have they gone to? . . . (*He studies the footprints of* GERDA *and* KAY.) Here? Yes! (*Going where he will discover* GERDA *and* KAY.) . . . Or . . . (*On* WENKI'S *and* STORYTELLER'S *track.*) Ah! They've gone here! (*Following tracks of* WENKI *and* STORYTELLER.) Haha! We'll find you! (*Calling.*) Come, Snow Queen! (*Exit* L.)

KAY: Come, Gerda, hurry, hurry!

They exit. The wind continues to howl.

BLACKOUT

SCENE 6

GRANNY'S GARRET

GRANNY'S *garret looking almost as in the first scene. Only now there is no snow on the roofs. It is a clear April day, drawing to its close; soon it will start getting dark. There are no flowers on the rose-tree.*

The room is empty. After a short time quick steps on the stair. There is a knock at the door, loud, impatient . . . another knock. . . . The door opens: WENKI *looks into the room, enters.*

WENKI (*out of breath*): Gerda! Gerda! (*She quickly goes through the room and looks into the adjoining room—disappointed.*) Oh!

(*The* PRINCE *enters running, out of breath too.*)

PRINCE: Is she here?

WENKI: No.

(*Quick steps outside, four feet this time, and the* STORY-TELLER *enters with the* PRINCESS.)

STORYTELLER: Found her?

PRINCE: Not yet.

PRINCESS: What did I say! If you had only listened. . . .

WENKI (*suddenly*): Look! (*She rushes to the table.*) A letter! (*She reads with difficulty.*) 'Chi-l-dr-en.'

PRINCE (*snatching it from her and continuing*): . . . 'There are rolls in the cupboard, butter, cream and honey. Eat and don't wait for me. I hope you will come today. It has been so sad without you. Granny.'

PRINCESS: What did I tell you? (*She turns away towards the window.*) Gerda never came back.

STORYTELLER: That's that. (*He sighs and looks at the withered rose-tree.*)

(*A long silence. Twilight.*)

PRINCE: It's getting dark.

STORYTELLER: Granny should be home soon.

(*The* RAVENS *suddenly alight on the window-sill.*)

KARL: Kl*a*ra—this is Gerda's Granny's window!

KLARA: D*a*rling K*a*rl discovered it *a*t *o*nce.

KARL: Ha-ha!

KLARA: L*o*vely!

KARL: Gr*a*nd!—Gr*a*nd!

PRINCE (*crossly to the* RAVENS):   Stop your chattering! Gerda and Kay are still lost.

KARL: S*a*d—

KLARA: S*a*d—

BOTH: Al*a*rming—

KLARA: S*a*d—

KARL: S*a*d—

KLARA: S*a*d—

BOTH: Al*a*rming—

KARL: S*a*d!

WENKI (*loudly*):   Shut up!—Or I'll shoot you! Yes, I shall!

BOTH (*almost inaudible*):   Alarming—sad . . .

(*A long silence. The* STORYTELLER *rises and lights the lamp.*)

STORYTELLER: It's quite dark.

WENKI (*to* STORYTELLER):   Oh stop moaning! If only your stupid feet hadn't moaned so much we would have got to the Far North and found her. Oh Crappity! Why didn't I go myself! I'll go now. I'm not afraid of the Snow Queen. I'll lead a new expedition to the North Pole itself. I'll track Gerda's footprints in the snow and far, far, far away up on the icy top of the World. . . .

STORYTELLER (*interrupting her*):   . . . Shsh! (*He gets to his feet.*)

(*They all listen to hurried footsteps coming up the stair. The door flies open and* GRANNY *comes in.*)

GRANNY: Children! You, back at last! Kay! Gerda! (*She stops.*) Oh! (*Pause.*) No. . . . (*Looking round.*) Two ravens? A Prince and Princess? And . . . Ah! Mr. Storyteller! (*She runs to the* STORYTELLER.) Mr. Storyteller, you have brought me news of Kay and Gerda? They are coming? (*Pause.*) Where are they?

STORYTELLER (*awkwardly*):   Well . . . Granny . . . I'm afraid we don't know. As a matter of fact . . . we didn't find them.

GRANNY (*gently*):   Oh! (*She sits down in silence as they all watch her, miserably.*) Every evening when I come home, and see our dark window from the yard, I think: perhaps they have come, and are only tired, and have fallen asleep. . . . And I go up—run into the room—nobody's there. I look into every corner—perhaps they are hiding, just to surprise me—nobody! . . . But tonight I saw the window lit. Thirty years fell off my shoulders, and I ran upstairs, came in . . . and the thirty years are back on me. . . . (*She rises.*)

WENKI (*in a temper*):   Sit down, Grandmother, dear Granny, and don't make me weep. I hate it! Sit down, or else I shall shoot everybody with my pistol!

(WENKI *points pistol at everybody.* GRANNY *quickly sits down.*)

(*Continuing, warmly.*) Don't be afraid, Granny. Everybody except you, of course.

GRANNY (*smiling*):   Now I recognise you from Mr. Storyteller's letter. . . . You are Wenki the Robber Girl. . . .

But now you must sit down comfortably like Karl and Klara.

KARL AND KLARA: *Ra-ta*!

GRANNY: I shall make you some tea. You must not look so sad. Everything will turn out all right.

STORYTELLER (*sadly*):   Perhaps.

GRANNY: They will come back soon.

STORYTELLER (*sadly*):   Perhaps.

WENKI (*losing her temper again*):   Perhaps!! (*Thumping the table with her fist.*) Don't just sit there saying, 'Perhaps! Perhaps!' I can't stand it! I won't stand it! *Do* something! Tell us a story, if that's all you're good for. Tell us a story to make us feel gay or . . . One! . . . A happy one. . . . Two! . . . A good one. . . . (*Aiming pistol.*)

STORYTELLER (*quickly*):   Once-upon-a-time-there-were . . . some steps—in fact a lot of steps, a whole family of them; and taken all together they became a stair. And they lived all together in a large house, stretching from the basement up to the attic. Now, the first-floor steps used to squeak boastfully to the second-floor steps, and the second-floor steps boasted to the third-floor steps . . . and so on. But when it came to the last steps leading to the attic they had no one above them to boast to. So they squeaked to themselves, 'We are the highest steps of all, and we are nearest the sky.' But, on the whole, they got along well together and creaked loudly and happily when somebody walked upstairs. (*He stops.*) Listen! . . . Granny. . . . Children. . . . Listen! Our steps are creaking now. . . . Somebody is coming. . . . Listen! . . . The fifth-floor steps are creaking. . . . They are coming! (*Creaking steps—then silence.*)
     (*They all get up expectantly.*)

78

They must have reached the top. They are out there now, and going to surprise us. I'm sure they . . .

(*The door bursts open and the* SNOW QUEEN *and the* CHAN-CELLOR *come in. The* RAVENS *disappear from the window.*)

SNOW QUEEN (*breaking the silence*): Where is Kay? Give me the boy—or I shall turn you all into ice.

GRANNY: But . . . the boy isn't here. . . .

SNOW QUEEN (*fiercely*): You are hiding him here some-where. I feel it. (*Moving about restlessly.*) Kay! Come out! I have come for you. You belong to me now. Kay! . . . Kay!

(*The* CHANCELLOR *who has been searching the rooms comes back in.*)

CHANCELLOR: The boy is not here.

SNOW QUEEN: Not here? (*Then she smiles.*) Then I know where to find him. (*Gliding towards door.*) And when I find him I will . . .

(WENKI *throws herself against the door, cutting off the* SNOW QUEEN. *The* PRINCE *and* PRINCESS *follow suit and all three join hands, courageously barring the* SNOW QUEEN'S *exit.*)

WENKI: No!

PRINCE AND PRINCESS: No!

SNOW QUEEN (*stopping*): Remember—I have only to wave my hand, and complete silence will reign here—for centuries!

WENKI: Wave away! We'll not let you leave this room!

PRINCE AND PRINCESS: No!

(*The* SNOW QUEEN *looks towards the window. She waves her hand and for a moment the wind howls and the light flickers. The* SNOW QUEEN *swiftly moves to the window—but the children arrive there first and bar the window.*)

79

PRINCE: You shan't find Kay!

   (*The door opens,* KAY *and* GERDA *are standing just inside the door.*)

SNOW QUEEN (*triumphantly*):   Shan't I! Kay!

THE CHILDREN: Gerda!

GRANNY AND STORYTELLER: Kay!

SNOW QUEEN: Kay . . . now you will come back with me.

KAY AND GERDA: No.

SNOW QUEEN: You must come back with me.

KAY (*advances one step*):   Go!

SNOW QUEEN (*in cold fury*):   Would you defy me? If you come another step I shall cut you to pieces with my north wind!

   (KAY *takes another step. The* SNOW QUEEN *waves her hands —the light flickers—the wind howls more than ever before— the light becomes normal again.* KAY *stands unperturbed.*)

   Kay, you are mine.

KAY (*advancing another step*):   You must go!

SNOW QUEEN: Haah! . . .

   (*She cries out in anger and frustration, and waves her hand. There is a sudden darkness—the sound of broken glass—the lamp goes out—the wind howls and whistles.*)

WENKI (*in the dark*):   Close the window! Hold the door.

PRINCE AND PRINCESS (*in the dark*):   We're holding it!

GRANNY: Don't be frightened! I'll light the lamp! I'll light the lamp!

   (*As she lights the lamp, they see that the* SNOW QUEEN *and the* CHANCELLOR *have gone;* WENKI *and the* PRINCE *and* PRINCESS *guard the door and* KAY *stands where he was.*)

ALL: Oh!

GERDA (*running to him*):   Kay!

PRINCESS: Where has she gone?

KLARA (*appearing at the window*): Her Majesty ...

KARL (*appearing at the window*): ... And His Excellency.

KLARA: They have departed rather hurriedly, going northwards on a black cloud.

KARL: On a black cloud.

WENKI: Hurrah! We defeated them.

KARL AND KLARA: Hurrah! Hurrah!

GRANNY: Oh! How glad I am!

KAY AND GERDA: Granny! (*They rush to her arms.*) We're back!

GERDA: He had a heart of ice but it melted!

KAY: And then I danced with polar bears ...

GERDA: ... and then we ran and ran ...

KAY: ... and we rode on the back of a reindeer, Granny.

GRANNY: And you're back! And you're back. (*Hugging them.*)

WENKI: I'm so happy I'll cry ... if I don't dance or *do* something. . . .

PRINCE AND PRINCESS: Kay! Gerda!

(*They all join hands and dance round* KAY *and* GERDA. *The music of the organ-grinder's tune comes into the dance.*)

STORYTELLER (*suddenly*): Look! Look!

(*He points to the roses and they all stop and look.*)

GRANNY: Our rose-tree! It's flowering again!

(*They all look at it.*)

PRINCESS: But how beautiful!

(*Organ-grinder's tune continues.*)

GRANNY: What can it mean?

STORYTELLER: It can only mean one thing: that we are all going to be happy together again.

GRANNY: And look!

STORYTELLER: What next?

GRANNY: The kettle is boiling! Tea! Tea, children!

ALL: Tea!

(*They all gather round the fire, chattering and getting cups while the* STORYTELLER *comes forward on tip toe doing his own little dance. The organ-grinder's music fades.*)

STORYTELLER (*quietly to the audience*):   That's that!

GERDA (*suddenly noticing his absence*):   Mr. Storyteller!

GRANNY: Mr. Storyteller! Don't you want your tea?

STORYTELLER: Did I ever refuse a cup of tea? No! But first I have something to do. I have finished my story happily; but remember this is not just a story—it's a play! And my friends are still watching me out there. (*Pointing into the audience.*)

GERDA: What friends?

STORYTELLER: Out there! The people who watched you. See! They are still watching, and they won't go away till I say so. Nothing can happen without me.

GERDA: Can't I say good-bye to them too?

STORYTELLER: Perhaps, but after me.

KAY (*eagerly*):   Can I say good-bye?

STORYTELLER: Yes, perhaps, but . . .

WENKI: Can I . . .? (*The children gradually push forward.*)

STORYTELLER: Yes, but . . .

GRANNY: Let's all say good-bye!

STORYTELLER (*controlling the pushing children*):   Alright, alright! But it is my play and I am going to end it my way.

ALL: What way?

(*The* STORYTELLER *gathers them all around him.*)

STORYTELLER: Ready! With me!

(They all dance.)
Snip! Snap! Snooper!
ALL: Pooper! Bazalooper!
STORYTELLER :   Snip! Snap! Snooper!
ALL: CRIPPITY! CRAPPITY! BOOM!

FINAL CURTAIN

MUSIC FOR THE PLAY
Composed by HENRY BOYS

THE STORYTELLER'S TUNE

THE BARREL-ORGAN TUNE

Now the frost-grips all the earth-, The birds be-gin - to
Tears which fall - and freeze till all - As snow flakes fill - the

cry. *(Repeat tune)* So all - the snow flakes are tears that are
sky.

Si-lent-ly gli - ding by For un-less - God's

sun will bless- our earth The birds- must die.